A Muslim Boy's Guide
to
Life's BIG Changes

Sami Khan

Ta-Ha Publishers Ltd.

Published by:
Ta-Ha Publishers Ltd.
Unit 4, The Windsor Centre
Windsor Grove, West Norwood
London, SE27 9NT, UK
www.tahapublishers.com

Written by: Sami Khan
Edited by: Muhammed Abrar Aziz
Cover Design: Mariama Janneh

A catalogue record of this book is available from the British Library.
ISBN: 978-1-84200-072-4

Printed and bound by: Mega Basim, Turkey

In memory of Ammaar Al-Ani
Our worlds may have divided us but our bond is forever
strong. May Allah ﷻ ease the pain of all those who love
you. (Ameen)

Jazaka'Allah to my big sis' and her 'wizard' friend for
their time and efforts and to all my young brothers who
read through the draft.

CONTENTS

I see that Allah has placed light in your heart
so do not extinguish it with the darkness
of disobedience.
(Imam Malik)

To my younger brother,

As salam alaikum,

Congratulations! You are no longer considered a little boy but rather a growing young man.

Your interests and activities are changing and you want to spend more time around your friends. You feel full of energy and want to try out lots of different things in life for yourself. After all, this is a fast-changing and exciting time. However, these years can also be testing ones as life at school, with your friends, may be very different to life at home and you may end up feeling confused about how to behave.

This book will, insha'Allah, help you to focus on the issues that are important for you as a young Muslim so that you do the right thing whilst making the most of these exciting years.

In short, the best advice I can give you is to '**Stop, think and question all that you do in your life.**' May Allah guide you through the coming years and make them easy for you – Ameen.

Wasalam,
Sami

1. Your Beliefs

The word 'Islam' means peace and obedience. It is made up of five basic pillars:

1. Shahadah: Statement of Belief
2. Salah: Five times daily prayer
3. Zakah: Giving of our wealth to the less fortunate
4. Sawm: Fasting in Ramadan
5. Hajj: Visiting Allah's House

At this stage of your life, you will need to be most aware of *shahadah, salah* and *sawm* for your daily life.

The first part of Shahadah is believing in the Oneness of Allah or tawheed. This means believing that there is only one Allah who has no partners or family; that Allah always has been and always will be; that He created everything and there is none like Him.

Scientists can boast about their achievements but the fact is that they cannot even create a single atom from nothing let alone the whole complex and beautiful universe that Allah alone has created. The opposite of tawheed is shirk, which means not believing in the Oneness of Allah and associating Him with someone or something else. This is the most grave and unforgivable sin in Islam. So, whenever you are facing a hard time, remember that Allah is the best friend and helper you could have.

Allah has given us so much and in order to show Him how grateful we are and how much we love Him, we must pray or perform salah five times a day. Salah is a chance for you to take time out from the routine of the day and become closer to Allah. It is a time for you to show your gratitude, ask forgiveness for your sins, ask for help, guidance and direction.

> The Prophet ﷺ said, "A person who has missed a single prayer is like someone who has lost all his wealth."
> (Ibn Hibban)

Ideally, you should have started to pray from the age of seven and certainly from the age of ten. If you haven't then it is never too late to start because Allah is very Kind and Forgiving. It is very important that you take the time out of your schedule to offer your salah at the right time, whether you are at home or at school or out and about.

During school hours, you will have to pray Dhuhr salah. If there isn't already a room set aside for doing salah in, then organize a polite meeting with the Head to arrange a room for you to pray in during lunch. This will benefit not only you and your friends but also future Muslim students at the school.

Performing the midday salah in congregation on Friday is called Jumu'ah. This is a duty that must be upheld by all Muslim men, so you must make every effort to attend Jumu'ah prayers. It is a great time to meet other Muslims and a chance to learn something useful by listening to the khutbah or sermon.

It is a grave sin to miss three Jumu'ah prayers in a row: Abu Ja'd ﷺ reported that the Holy Prophet ﷺ said: "Whoever misses three Fridays (prayers) consecutively due to laziness, Allah seals his heart." (an-Nasai)

Another act of worship that brings us closer to Allah is fasting during the month of Ramadan (sawm). You must fast as soon as you reach the age of puberty, but it is good practise for you to begin before then.

By not eating and drinking during the day, we learn to think of those that are less fortunate than us and to give generously. But while you are fasting, you also have to be careful of your actions, intentions and the way you speak. There is no point in not eating and drinking if you are going to lie and swear.

> The Prophet ﷺ said, "Whoever does not give up lying and cheating, Allah does not require him to give up eating and drinking."
> (Muslim)

Ramadan is known as the Month of the Qur'an since it was first revealed during this month. The Prophet ﷺ recommended that we read the whole Qur'an once during Ramadan. Many men attend the mosque for nightly sunnah prayers called tarawih during which the Qur'an is recited. If you are able to, you should try to attend the tarawih salah at your local mosque.

Another very important belief is that the life of this world (Dunya) is temporary and there is an eternal Life after Death (Akhirah). Our actions in this life will determine whether we will be punished in Hell or rewarded with the bounties of Paradise. That is why it is very important to take care of each and every one of your actions because you will be asked about these on the Day of Judgement.

It is very important that you perform your salah regularly and fast during the month of Ramadan at this age because the Prophet ﷺ explained that Allah is more pleased with any good deeds that we do during our youth than at any other time.

2. Your Friends

You will meet lots of different kinds of boys at school and you may choose to spend your time with some of them both in and outside of school. You might not think that it matters too much who your friends are but it is vital to choose the correct friendship group, as friends can either be your strength or your weakness.

Think about it...as you spend more time with your friends, you find that their views and ideas have an effect on you. They begin to influence the way you look, speak and behave. I can guarantee that your friends will leave a lifetime impression on you, so be careful of who you choose to have as your friends.

> The Prophet ﷺ said, "A person is likely to follow the faith of his friend, so look whom you befriend."
> (Abu Da'ud)

Those who choose to be disrespectful to their elders and spend their time in un-Islamic places doing un-Islamic things are really not worth having as friends. They may distract you from your studies, from religion and perhaps pressure you into looking and acting like someone you're not, just to fit in with them.

You should try to keep in the company of those who understand the importance of being good Muslims and taking care of their every action. You see, at this age your friends are in the unique position of having a big influence on you and it may be easy to forget what your parents have taught you.

It is a mistake to try and lead two lives – one at home in order to please your family and a different one at school to make you popular with your friends. Remember that Allah is everywhere and knows everything.

You might enjoy your popularity with the 'in' crowd at school for a short while, but you will ultimately be the loser if you are not true to yourself.

Of course, it's not always as simple as it sounds and there will be times when you feel split between your school friends and your religion. It can be difficult to stand up to some peers, but Allah has given you the intelligence to know right from wrong, so you should fight temptation and stand up for what you believe in.

Just remember to...

Surround yourself with good and suitable friends who will offer you support;

Be proud of who you are and don't feel intimidated by those who you know are in the wrong;

Stop, think and question your actions. It is all too easy to do things in the heat of the moment that you later regret;

Seek advice and support from your parents, uncles, older brothers and cousins who have all been through what you are facing;

Always turn to Allah for strength and guidance to do the right thing. At the same time, try to learn more about Islam. It is not just a set of rules and you can find plenty of excellent and relevant advice about what to do in difficult times and situations.

3. Your Time

Part of growing up is about having your independence and freedom to be able to meet with your friends outside of school time. There is no harm in this so long as you stick to some simple rules.

 You must always ask your parents' permission before going out. If they say that you can't go somewhere or do something, then respect their decision.

 Always let them know who you will be with, where you are and what you will be doing.

You must ensure that you return home at the time your parents tell you to. It is very important that you do not break your parents' trust.

When you are spending time with your friends, make sure that you have safe halal fun that does not cause anyone any distress.

Wandering around the streets aimlessly or hanging out on street corners is a waste of time for you and a nuisance for other people. Amusement arcades, snooker halls and the bookies are no place for Muslims. The atmosphere in these places is often smoky and full of non-Muslims enjoying themselves whilst drinking alcohol.

As an alternative, why not try sport, whether it's cricket or football or anything else you enjoy? Not only is sport fun, it also helps to keep you in good shape, it teaches you to work as part of a team, disciplines you and is also a sunnah as the Holy Prophet ﷺ enjoyed some sports as well. Do bear in mind, though, that if you attend a gym or go to a swimming pool, the facilities should be for men only. Many sports centres have sessions specifically for men/boys.

As a Muslim, the masjid (mosque) should be a place that you visit frequently, preferably with other male members of your family. Praying salah at the masjid as opposed to performing it at home holds great reward.

> The Prophet ﷺ stated, "Prayer in congregation is more than 25 times more rewarding than prayer at home."
> (Bukhari and Muslim)

However, a masjid is not only a place of worship but also a social centre for Muslims, allowing people of all ages to get together. It is a place where you can meet other Muslim boys of a similar age and interests. It is also a place where you will feel a sense of community and belonging. Many masajid offer a variety of activities for young Muslims, but if your masjid doesn't, then you can always ask the management for group activities etc. to be arranged.

When you are at home, either alone or with friends, you should also try to spend your time sensibly. This means that you should not be listening to the latest rap tunes or any other un-Islamic form of music. Most types of lyrical music (Western/Bollywood/Bhangra) are not appropriate to listen to because of unsuitable themes and lyrics.

Music can be considered the adhan of the Shaytan and when the Holy Prophet ﷺ heard music he would cover his ears with his hands in disapproval.

You might think that you need such music to relax or even to do your homework and soon you find it difficult to do anything without having music on in the background. This is a shame because music containing bad lyrics can blacken your heart and distract you from doing your salah. If you would like to listen to something, then why not try listening to nasheeds which are a much better and halal form of entertainment.

Did you know that recent research shows young people spend as much as one-third of their lives solidly watching TV? Is that really how you want to spend your whole life? After all, when you spend so long just staring at the screen it must have a bad effect on you. When you watch actors or singers on TV or indeed on DVDs and in the cinema, behaving improperly, dressing immodestly and using bad language then after a while you think that it is OK to behave that way and you start to behave like that too. Having said that, there are a number of halal and informative programmes which you can watch on TV, if you wish.

Similarly, the internet can also be a useful source of information but it is all too easy to get involved in and lose track of time. Spending your time in chat rooms and downloading music are time wasting activities at the very least and can be dangerous.

Never give out your personal details over the net no matter how safe it seems.

Another thing you should be careful of is spending too much time playing video games either on a Playstation or X-box. This is not useful or educational. Many games are unsuitable because of their themes of violence and aggression.

Remember that you need to concentrate on your schoolwork now if you want to reach your goals and full potential later on in life. This is the only way that you will have a choice about what you want to do as a career even if career choices might seem a long way away at the moment.

> The Prophet ﷺ said, "Part of a person's being a good Muslim is his leaving alone that which does not concern him."
>
> (Tirmidhi)

Be sure to balance your schoolwork, your religious duties and your leisure time. The keys to spending your time wisely are:

To remember Allah throughout the day by praying salah and reading Qur'an daily.

To leave, or at least spend the minimum amount of time on, those things that distract you from your religious duties as well as your studies.

4. How You Can Become Closer to Allah

There are many ways in which you can spend your time constructively and become closer to Allah.

Reading the QUR'AN

The Qur'an is the Word of Allah which was revealed to our Beloved Prophet Muhammad ﷺ through the Angel Jibra'il عليه السلام. There are two reasons why you should read it regularly.

Simply reading the Qur'an in Arabic with your full attention is in itself an act of worship and will bring you closer to Allah.

The Qur'an is a guide given to us by Allah and so it contains plenty of useful and relevant advice about how best to live our lives.

So, by reading it, understanding what it says and acting upon it you will become closer to Allah and insha'Allah a better Muslim. Even reading a few lines regularly every day, you will find that you can finish the whole Qur'an at least twice in a year.

It is also important to memorise small verses from the Qur'an so that you can recite them in your salah. The Holy Prophet ﷺ said, "The person who has nothing of the Qur'an inside him is like an empty or ruined house." (Tirmidhi)

DU'A

Du'a, which means 'calling upon', is a very personal way of communicating with Allah. You can choose what you say and which language you say it in, but there are some recommended ways in which to make du'a.

The Prophet ﷺ used to make du'a by facing the Qibla and raising his cupped hands towards the sky. When you make du'a, it is good to thank Allah for all that He has given you and to send salat and salam to the Holy Prophet ﷺ and his family. You can ask for anything as long as it is halal and does not involve asking Allah to harm or hurt anyone else. You can ask for forgiveness, strength, guidance, good health, good exam results, good things in this world and in the Akhirah. Be sure to pray for your loved ones, including those who have passed away. You can pray for those that are less fortunate than you and especially those who are suffering as a result of war, natural disasters etc.

You must not lose hope if your du'a is not answered immediately. If that was the case it would mean Allah would become our servant waiting for our requests instead of our Master. For your du'a to be answered you have to work towards becoming closer to Allah. Remember Allah is the best of planners. Your prayers will, insha'Allah, be accepted when the time is right but you have to be patient.

DHIKR

Another way of becoming closer to Allah is through dhikr (the remembrance of Allah).

Allah has mentioned in the Quran that:
'Remember Me and I shall remember you.'
(2:152)

You can do dhikr at any time of the day, while you are walking, sitting or even when you can't sleep. You can spend as little as a few seconds reciting a few words either in your mind, on your fingers or on a tasbih. The following words carry a great reward:

SubhanAllah – Glory be to Allah
Alhamdulillah – All praise and thanks is due to Allah
La ilaha illallah – There is no god but Allah
Allahu Akbar – Allah is the Greatest
Astaghfirullah – I seek Allah's forgiveness.

By performing a SUNNAH

The word sunnah means 'practice'. When you carry out a sunnah you are copying the actions and sayings of the Prophet Muhammad ﷺ who is the best example of how we should behave. By following the noble practices of our Prophet ﷺ we are in fact becoming better Muslims.

It does not have to be difficult or time consuming to perform a sunnah. For example, the Prophet ﷺ would always begin his meal with the words 'Bismillahir rahmanir raheem' and eat with his hands. He would always finish his food and he never criticised the taste of food.

It is little actions such as these which will help others to warm to Islam and earn you a great reward from Allah.

SADAQAH

Sadaqah is when you do something generous for others only for the pleasure of Allah. It may be as simple as smiling at someone to cheer them up, picking up litter from the street or perhaps not buying some sweets for yourself one day and giving the money to charity. When you do something selfless for someone else then Allah is very pleased and He rewards you both in this world and in the Hereafter.

> The Prophet ﷺ said, "...Sadaqah destroys sins as water extinguishes fire..." (Mishkat)

5. The People Around You

Part of being a good Muslim is to balance our duties towards Allah and our responsibilities towards the people that we come into contact with every day. But what are these responsibilities?

PARENTS

To please Allah you must treat your parents with the utmost love and respect. Your mother endured the pain of carrying you inside her for nine months and since the day you were born, she continues to give up so much just to make sure that you are safe, healthy and happy. Your father spends his day caring and providing for you. They both spend every waking moment worrying about you and wanting the best for you. Therefore, under no circumstances should you ever be rude to them, disobey them (unless they ask you to do something that goes against Islam) or answer back to them.

If you want to enter Jannah then you must love and care for your mother as she has done for you. The Prophet ﷺ also highlighted the importance of pleasing your father: "A father's pleasure is Allah's pleasure, and a father's displeasure is Allah's displeasure." (Tirmidhi).

> The Prophet ﷺ said, "Paradise lies beneath the feet of your mother." (an-Nasa'i)

If you want to be successful in this life and in the Akhirah then you must take care of your parents; the two most important people in your life.

SIBLINGS

You must respect others if you want them to respect you, and that applies especially to those that you live with, regardless of whether they are older or younger than you. It is worth remembering that your actions, especially negative behaviour, will most certainly have an impact on your entire family.

Brothers and sisters who see you arguing with your parents will be badly affected by the tension in the house. It is selfish and narrow minded to think 'It's my life' and 'What's it got to do with anyone else?' because Muslim families are close-knit.

If you are older than your brothers and sisters, then make sure that you behave well around them as they will turn to you as an example and role model. If your siblings are older than you, then you must treat them with respect and speak politely to them.

TEACHERS

You should show your teachers great respect because, after your parents, it is your teachers that care about your welfare and education. You should avoid playing the class joker just to impress your friends. Teachers are valuable people who are there for you, not just for school matters but also personal concerns.

GIRLS

You may find that your non-Muslim friends are starting to take an interest in girls. You may have noticed that some girls are changing too - their dress sense may seem more mature and they too seem to enjoy the company of the boys. It is natural to have such feelings at this age but you must be absolutely clear that it is against the teachings of Islam to mix freely with girls. You must not laugh or joke with girls and under no circumstance should you ever be alone with a girl. In fact, you should lower your gaze when there are girls around. You must never join in with boys who boast about being with girls or comment and laugh at girls because of their appearances.

IN GENERAL

You should be polite and respectful to everyone you meet regardless of age, race or religion. You may not agree with everything that everyone says but you need to remain calm and remember not to get angry when you talk with others. If you cannot think of anything good or positive to say then it is better not to say anything at all. Try not to backbite (talk behind people's backs) about others, swear or talk loudly.

This respect also extends to all of Allah's creations, including animals and the environment in which we live. Islam teaches us that we should treat animals with love and kindness and to make sure that no harm comes to them. If you abuse your surroundings and create unnecessary pollution and waste, then you are being ungrateful to Allah for all that He has given you. This means that you should be careful about not wasting things like water and paper.

Insha'Allah, you will find that if you treat everyone with respect then you will also be respected by everyone.

6. Your Image

The image and attitude that you create for yourself sends out a message to everyone you meet. Does your wardrobe consist entirely of designer labels? Are you sporting the latest haircut that is carefully held in place with far too much gel? When you speak do you speak harshly or even use the odd swear word? Is your mobile phone always stuck to your ear?

It seems that you are modelling yourself around football players, pop stars and other celebrities. But are they really the best role model for you? As a Muslim, you should ask yourself whether your dress code, language and values are dictated by Islam or by celebrities.

Islam teaches you to dress modestly and decently and in a way that does not intimidate other people. Your clothes should not be too expensive, made of silk or resemble feminine clothing. The area from your navel to your knees is called your awrah and should always be fully covered in a loose garment in front of everyone including your mother, sister and other males. This means that sharing a communal shower or showering in a public place is strictly haram. When you play sports or go swimming then your awrah must be completely covered.

It is also haram to change your appearance in any way. This means that it is not allowed to have any part of your body pierced, to have any tattoos (even the temporary kind) or to dye your hair permanently. Gold jewellery is strictly haram for men.

Your hair should be kept well combed and neat and it should not be kept long. It is wajib to keep a beard and it shows that you are proud to be a Muslim. It is sinful to get rid of it once it has grown.

When you speak, you must always use decent language and talk politely and respectfully with everyone. The Prophet ﷺ always smiled both at people that he knew and also people that he did not know because he was a very pleasant and good natured person.

You are judged by the way that you behave with other people not by the number of accessories that you have. If your parents do not feel it necessary for you to own a mobile phone or iPod, then respect their wishes because they know best. Be honest, do you want a gadget simply to keep up with everyone else or do you really need one?

> Allah does not look at your outward appearance but only your hearts and deeds.
> (Muslim)

So next time you go out, think about the message that you wish to send out to the world about you. Do you want to be seen as a moody fashion-obsessed guy or a decent young man whom it would be a pleasure to meet?

7. Changes in Your Body

You will find that there are some changes occurring in your body now. This process is called puberty and takes place between the age of 11 and 15, lasting between 2-4 years. So what are these changes?

You will notice that your body's shape and size is changing. You may gain weight and begin to develop muscles. Your shoulders and chest broaden and you begin to grow taller.

You will find thicker, darker hair growth on your legs, feet, arms, underarms, face and your private area (pubic hair) and perhaps also on your chest and back.

Your glands produce more oil and so you will begin to sweat more. Your hair and face may be oilier than before and you might get spots or even acne on your face, shoulders and chest.

You will also experience a change in your voice. Your 'voice breaks' as a result of your voice box (larynx) getting bigger. To begin with, you may find that the pitch of your voice is slightly higher at times. Once this settles down your voice will sound deeper and louder.

During puberty you will find that your bones are growing at such a fast rate that your muscles become stretched and cause pain, especially in your legs.

Some boys experience swollen, tender breasts, this is quite normal and can last up to 18 months.

All these changes are a blessing from Allah and mark your move from childhood into adulthood. Watching your body change can leave you feeling a little unsettled and worried. You may find that you feel a little anxious and self-conscious as you may not be developing at the same rate as your friends. Remember, everyone matures at a different rate. It will happen: it's just a matter of when.

Now that you are reaching the age of maturity you may be taking more of an interest in the way you look in the hope of impressing members of the opposite sex. You may find that you are thinking of girls in a different way than before.

These feelings are natural but as a Muslim you should try to curb these thoughts. You may find that you are thinking of girls both during the day and perhaps while you are sleeping, through your dreams. As a result of these dreams (known as wet dreams) you might find that when you wake your bedding and clothing is a little wet as through these dreams the private part has released a sticky fluid (semen).

If you experience a wet dream and discharge of semen you must take a special bath known as ghusl to purify yourself. You must perform ghusl as soon as possible otherwise you cannot perform salah, read or touch the Qur'an. Remember that any bedding and clothing which has become soiled by the discharge must be washed thoroughly. Ghusl must also be carried out in the event of a discharge of semen without a dream.

While wet dreams are normal, it is best to curb any un-Islamic thoughts. As a Muslim, you should never watch films which show men and women acting out a physical relationship with one another. Looking at magazines and newspapers that feature pictures of scantly dressed women is haram. Logging onto adult web sites which promote such indecencies is also haram. Looking at other men who are not dressed is haram. Using your mobile phone to ring up a chat line is haram. They are all considered as zina or adultery which is a very serious sin in Islam as your eyes and ears are doing things which they should not be. Any such acts are haram whether they are carried out in secret or in public. Remember that Allah sees and hears ALL things.

It is probably best to speak to someone who has dealt with these changes, your father, an uncle, older brother – there is always someone you can talk to who will understand and help you through this time.

8. Taking Care of Your Body

Your body is a trust from Allah. You must look after it well because on the Day of Judgement you will be asked about how you treated it. Personal hygiene is extremely important for a Muslim so it is essential that you take good care of this by showering/bathing regularly and performing wudu before you worship Allah.

Sometimes you might feel like not bothering to do your wudu but did you know that by performing wudu regularly, not only are your sins washed away, but those parts of the body that you wet will shine on the Day of Judgement? (Muslim). Wudu refreshes you, keeps your body temperature regulated and also removes poisonous gases from the body.

In addition to washing your mouth out regularly during wudu, it is also a good idea to use a miswak (a special soft tooth stick) as was the custom of the Prophet ﷺ. This is an excellent way of keeping the mouth clean and smelling fresh.

It is important that you keep your nails short because dirt that collects under your fingernails will end up in your mouth when you are eating. You also need to remove the hair under your arms and from your private parts by shaving regularly, but certainly no more than 40 days must pass before you do this or else you will be committing a sin. By shaving this hair you prevent bacteria from spreading and sweat from building.

Make sure that you change your clothes regularly whenever you shower as this will help keep you smelling fresh and clean. Using an anti-bacterial soap while showering will often help with this.

You will need to perform ghusl each time you become unclean through discharge and it is also recommended for all Muslim men to perform ghusl on Friday before Jumu'ah salah.

HOW TO PERFORM GHUSL:

Start your ghusl by making an intention or niyah to purify yourself. Then you should wash both hands up to and including the wrists, followed by your private parts. You should then perform wudu. After wudu, you need to pour water three times over your head, three times over your right shoulder, three times over the left shoulder and finally over your entire body. You must make sure that by the end of your ghusl not even a single hair or place of a hair on your body is left dry otherwise the ghusl will be incomplete.

> Allah is Pure and Clean and He loves cleanliness and purity.
> (Mishkat)

As well as taking care of your body from the outside, it is important that everything you eat is halal.

This means that you should be careful about what you eat especially when you are eating out. Meat or chicken burgers from non-halal restaurants are haram. Saying *Bismillah* over a cooked burger before taking a bite does not make it halal. Sometimes, it may not be obvious that something is haram, for example, sweets that contain gelatine are haram because gelatine is an animal product. Always be careful about reading the labels of food that you eat and if in doubt then leave it.

Your body is growing and changing fast and you will need to eat a balanced diet which will help towards building a healthy body. Your body will need a balance of proteins such as meat, fish, eggs and milk and carbohydrates such as rice, bread and potatoes. Try to cut down on fatty, processed and junk foods and fizzy drinks which are not good for your health and will not help you concentrate in your studies.

It is also important to do a moderate amount of exercise which will help to keep you fit and prevent you from becoming overweight. However, be careful about overdoing it as too much exercise can be dangerous (especially lifting heavy weights) and leave you sore and exhausted. There is no need to buy supplements and body building drinks; your body will grow when it is good and ready.

Some of the boys in your school may be smoking cigarettes or drinking alcohol. Smoking cigarettes is anything but cool. It damages the heart and lungs, poisons the blood and can cause death. Once you become addicted to smoking it is very difficult to kick the habit, so stay well clear of the 'cancer stick' which will lead you to a life of misery.

Drinking alcohol in public or in secret is haram. One drink is just as haram as many drinks. Alcohol has numerous devastating effects on the body and mind, as well as resulting in badly affected relationships. It will cloud your mind and impair your judgement and you may end up doing things under the influence of alcohol that you will later regret. That is why Allah has categorically prohibited the consumption, buying, selling and handling of alcohol.

> The Prophet ﷺ said, "...He who drinks wine in this world and dies while he is addicted to it, not having repented, will not be given a drink in the Hereafter."
> (Muslim)

You must be clear that drugs like alcohol are haram. They are strictly forbidden for all Muslims as they are considered a poison. Don't feel pressured into trying them just because other boys are. They are dirty and expensive habits that will ruin your life. Drug users and alcoholics will go to all lengths in order to raise the cash needed, even if that means stealing from their loved ones. Drugs and alcohol not only destroy your health, but they play with your mind.

Those who choose to destroy their bodies in this way are sealing their hearts, as they begin to lose their Iman, their physical health and their mental health. Do you really want to spend the rest of your life in this state?

Remember that cleanliness is part of faith and that means outward and inward purity. A pure body will mean a pure heart and mind.

9. Parting Words

So we have taken a brief journey into what you can expect while you are growing up. It is understandable if you are feeling a little confused about your identity as a Muslim and daunted by the years ahead of you.

The best advice I can give you is to keep remembering Allah, remember Him through the good and happy times as well as the difficult times. Praying to Allah for guidance is always the right thing to do.

Friends are important, but they are not everything. You should aim to please Allah and your parents by always being mindful of your language, actions and behaviour. This will earn you respect.

Don't waste these precious years by slavishly becoming a follower of fashion, trends and images. Rise to the challenge, be your own person, set your own goals. Above all, be proud to be a young Muslim and stand up for your beliefs. Remember that Islam is about respect, kindness and peace.

I pray that Allah keeps you on the Right Path always and that Allah guides and blesses you in all that you do – Ameen.

10. Quick Quiz

Circle the answer that applies most to you and then see how you have done on page 48.

1. Are you careful about not buying or wearing designer labels?

    Always   Mostly

    Sometimes   Never

2. Do you perform salah five times a day?

    Always   Mostly

    Sometimes   Never

3. Are you careful about not listening to music which angers Allah?

    Always   Mostly

    Sometimes   Never

4. Are you careful about whom you choose to befriend?

    Always   Mostly

    Sometimes   Never

5. Do you read the Qur'an daily?

Always   Mostly

Sometimes   Never

6. Do you consider that Allah sees and hears all things that you do through the day and night?

Always   Mostly

Sometimes   Never

7. Do you avoid temptation by staying well clear of non-Islamic hangout places?

Always   Mostly

Sometimes   Never

8. Do you put your parents' view before your friends'?

Always   Mostly

Sometimes   Never

9. Are you careful about covering your awrah?

Always   Mostly

Sometimes   Never

Find which answer you have circled the most number of times and see what it says about you:

'Always' – Well done! You seem to be aware of your Islamic duties and are careful about fulfilling them. Keep it up!

'Mostly' – Good for you! You are mostly aware of what you should be doing, you just need to push yourself a bit more.

'Sometimes' – You do know right from wrong but you don't always practise it. Do you find yourself behaving differently around different people or in different places? Remember that Allah is everywhere. You have nothing to lose and everything to gain by doing the right thing.

'Never' – Well done for being honest. Try to make a small resolution at the beginning of each week or month and then stick to it. It will become easier to incorporate Islamic habits into your daily life.

WEAPON

MP 38 AND MP 40 SUBMACHINE GUNS

ALEJANDRO DE QUESADA

Series Editor Martin Pegler

First published in Great Britain in 2014 by Osprey Publishing,
PO Box 883, Oxford, OX1 9PL, UK
1385 Broadway, 5th Floor, New York, NY 10018, USA
E-mail: info@ospreypublishing.com

Osprey Publishing is part of Bloomsbury Publishing Plc

A CIP catalogue record for this book is available from the British
Library

Print ISBN: 978 1 78096 388 4
PDF ebook ISBN: 978 1 78096 389 1
ePub ebook ISBN: 978 1 78096 390 7

Index by Mark Swift
Typeset in Sabon and Univers
Battlescenes by Johnny Shumate
Cutaway by Alan Gilliland
Originated by PDQ Media, Bungay, UK
Printed in China through Worldprint Ltd

17 18   10 9 8 7 6 5 4 3 2

Osprey Publishing is supporting the Woodland Trust, the UK's
leading woodland conservation charity, by funding the dedication
of trees.

www.ospreypublishing.com

Author's dedication

This work is dedicated to a Fellow of the Company of Military
Historians and a dear friend, Ed Besch. For years Ed has told me
of his experiences in Vietnam and the various weapons he
encountered – including the MP 40. His fascination with military
history – especially his works covering the American Revolution
– is an inspiration.

Author's acknowledgements

I would like to thank the following individuals and institutions
that made this work possible: Ed Besch; Alex Cruiming; David
Persons; AdeQ Historical Archives; AdeQ Firearms Company;
Cody Images; Leroy Thompson; US Army Ordnance Museum;
National Museum of the Infantry; Imperial War Museum;
Canadian War Museum; Warsaw Uprising Museum; National
Archives and Records Administration (NARA); Library of
Congress; James D. Julia Inc.; Denix S.A.; and The Company of
Military Historians.

Editor's note

In this book, metric units of measurement are employed as the
Germans used metric during World War II. For ease of
comparison please refer to the following conversion table:

1km = 0.62 miles
1m = 1.09yd / 3.28ft
1cm = 0.39in
1mm = 0.04in
1kg = 2.20lb / 35.27oz

Front-cover images are courtesy of (top) AdeQ Historical Archives
and (bottom) Cody Images. The title page image is courtesy of
AdeQ Historical Archives; here, the user is holding the magazine
with his left hand for stability, though this practice is contrary to
what the manual specified. The correct manner was to hold the
magazine well for stability, rather than the magazine itself.

CONTENTS

INTRODUCTION

To understand fully the history of the MP 38 and MP 40, we need to reflect in general on the underlying principles of submachine guns (SMGs). In the modern world, the rationale behind SMGs has been slightly lost, at least in official military circles, owing to the ubiquity of the assault rifle, a weapon that manages to strike an effective balance between the range of a full-power rifle and the suppressive fire of an SMG. Yet if we dial back time to the beginning of World War II, the situation and the thinking were very different. Powerful, heavy and lengthy bolt-action rifles like the German Kar 98 and the British Short Magazine Lee-Enfield (SMLE) were dominant among an infantry still wedded to the idea that every soldier was a long-range marksman, picking off targets at the extremities of the battlefield. Time and changing conditions would transform this idea. Between the beginning of World War I and the early 1940s, combat experience yielded new data about the realities of small-arms actions. A fundamental conclusion was that in the real world soldiers rarely engaged targets at more than 300m, even though they were equipped with weapons capable of reaching out to well over double that distance. In actual fact, any human-sized target beyond 400m was difficult enough to see, let alone to shoot. Furthermore, many battlefield encounters involved small-arms exchanges at ranges of less than 100m. So if long-range accuracy was not as important as previously considered (except for snipers and heavier attrition weapons, such as machine guns), what were the critical factors for front-line soldiers?

The dynamics of combat shooting change profoundly at close ranges when compared to long-range engagements. Targets appear briefly between areas of cover, particularly in urban or forested areas. Considered aim is rarely possible, the soldier resorting instead to snap-shooting, often without the weapon properly mounted in the shoulder. Bolt-action rifles are poorly suited to this performance. Their length makes them unwieldy in confined terrain, and the need to operate the bolt mechanism means

4

that quick follow-up shots are problematic, if not impossible. SMGs, by contrast, are at their best at close ranges and in small spaces.

By firing pistol-calibre rounds, SMGs trade range (effective range is little more than 150m) for controllable (this word is key) full-auto fire, putting as many rounds as possible onto the target area in a fleeting window of time. The rapid fire they deliver compensates for imperfect aim. Most SMGs fire at rates of between 500 and 900rds/min, so even at the bottom of that range a one-second burst puts out eight rounds, the spread of shots increasing the likelihood of at least one hit on a moving or briefly exposed target. The ripples of fire are not only intrinsically suppressive, but they can also allow an individual soldier to engage multiple targets simultaneously and successfully. Visible impacts can also be 'walked' onto the target, meaning that shooting from the hip (a common situation in close-quarters actions) is more than just a 'spray and pray' approach. A high magazine capacity – 30–100 rounds, depending on the weapon and magazine type – ensures that there are usually plenty of rounds left for follow-up shots, as long as the soldier exercises some discipline with ammunition consumption and makes intelligent magazine changes. SMGs are by their very design typically compact weapons, hence their common use by vehicle and artillery crews, or by airborne troops.

The three main types of SMGs developed and used by Germany during World War II. From top to bottom: MP 38, MP 40 and MP 41. (AdeQ Historical Archives)

In close-quarters action, having something you can manoeuvre easily, while also putting out blistering fire, is a gift to battlefield survival, hence SMGs became a defining weapon type of World War II.

In this book, we focus our attention on two of the archetypal SMGs of this conflict – the German MP 38 and MP 40. Originating in the trenches of World War I, the concept of a multi-purpose SMG would reach a new standard with this pair of German designs, which would revolutionize infantry combat at the squad level. Widely issued to *Fallschirmjäger* (parachute infantry) owing to their portability and folding stocks, the MP 38 and MP 40 became the hallmarks of Germany's infantry section and platoon leaders; by the war's end the Germans were following the Soviet practice of issuing entire assault platoons with SMGs, these units being capable of delivering literally stunning levels of firepower.

The MP 38 and later the MP 40 remained the standard SMGs of the German armed forces throughout World War II, with total production numbering well over a million. Here we come upon another critical consideration regarding SMGs, and their role during the conflict. The sheer scale of World War II, and the need to arm effectively millions of hastily conscripted soldiers, meant that the combatant nations had to seek ways to rationalize production. Weapons had to be cheap and quick to turn out. Anything involving complex machining processes cost time and money most nations did not have, hence during World War II we tend to see SMGs become progressively cruder, while not necessarily diminishing their effectiveness. At the beginning of the conflict, for example, the United Kingdom had small stocks of the exquisitely machined Lanchester SMG, a true Rolls-Royce of weaponry. War conditions changed the game entirely, and from 1941 nearly four million crude tubular Sten guns were produced. Most of the Sten variants (especially the common Mk III) were almost laughably rudimentary when held up against the

A slabsided MP 40 showing the earlier MP 38-style charging handle. (AdeQ Historical Archives)

Lanchester, but the important point was that they worked and were in as many hands as possible. The MP 38 and MP 40 were also guns of the mass-production ethos. Much of our development story here considers how the demands of quality and quantity were balanced in these exceptional weapons.

The MP 38 and MP 40 earned their reputation in World War II, but it is often forgotten that they continued in use all over the world for many decades after 1945. All manufacture ceased with the capitulation of Germany in 1945, but many of the guns found their way into the hands of paramilitary and irregular forces, from Israel to Vietnam; the Norwegian armed forces continued to use them until the early 1990s, and examples and derivatives saw use in the Yugoslav wars of that decade.

The MP 38 and MP 40 eventually took on a life of their own – not only in the annals of firearms development and military history, but also in popular culture. Films, television programmes and, more recently, video games have helped to create a legend, making these weapons among the most recognizable of those used during World War II.

This MP 38-armed soldier has inserted magazines into his magazine pouch with the bottom ends facing upwards. (AdeQ Historical Archives)

DEVELOPMENT
A new breed of SMG

ORIGINS AND FORERUNNERS

During World War I the German Army recognized a need for a compact weapon offering a high volume of fire, suitable for close-range use in trench warfare and as an auxiliary defensive weapon for heavy-weapons crews. The first attempt to provide German troops with such a weapon was a special model of the 9mm Luger semi-automatic pistol with a 20.3cm barrel, an unusual 'snail' type 32-round drum magazine and a detachable shoulder stock. These 'Artillery' models were expensive to make and did not completely meet the desired requirements.

In late 1917 Hugo Schmeisser (1884–1953), then working at the Theodor Bergmann Waffenbau Abteilung, adopted features of various

A Weimar-era policeman is seen firing his MP 18.I using the snail-drum magazine commonly used with the Artillery Luger, 1920s. (AdeQ Historical Archives)

Developed by Theodor Bergmann during World War I, the MP 18.I started a revolution in SMG development. (Cody Images)

earlier designs of weapons and combined them into his own design. Using some of the general principles of the Italian Villar Perosa 9mm machine gun and the blowback action previously used in semi-automatic pistols such as the Walther Modell 4, Schmeisser designed the first true SMG, the Maschinenpistole 18.I (MP 18.I). Using the distinctive Luger snail-drum magazine, the MP 18.I would be issued to German non-commissioned officers (NCOs) in heavy-machine-gun sections as a defensive weapon, as well as to special infantry assault sections as a close-range offensive weapon.

The MP 18.I

The MP 18.I was introduced into service in 1918. Although MP 18.I production ended in the 1920s, the gun's design would form the basis of most SMGs manufactured between 1920 and 1960. The action was a straight blowback – the rearward force imparted by gas pressure upon the cartridge case after firing provided the motive power for the operating cycle. The bolt was not locked at the point of firing, and the inertia of the heavy bolt contained the force of the exploding cartridge long enough for the bullet to leave the barrel and for the chamber pressure to drop to a safe level. The MP 18.I offered full-automatic mode only. The weapon's cyclic rate was 350–450 shots per minute; this comparatively low cyclic rate allowed the shooter to fire single shots by quick release of the trigger after each shot.

Bergmann produced the weapon from the summer of 1918 until the Treaty of Versailles took effect in 1920. Production was more than 25,000 guns according to serial-number ranges. The Treaty of Versailles specified in its terms that Germany was not allowed to produce the SMG. After the treaty ended production, Schmeisser, now working with C.G. Haenel Waffenfabrik, obtained manufacturing rights for the gun and moved production to Haenel. There he continued to develop the design while Haenel did the development work on the weapon, made parts and converted the MP 18.I to a box-magazine feed. Examples converted to the modified feed by Haenel have 'C.G. Haenel, Waffenfabrik Suhl' marked on the magazine well.

Because of the Versailles Treaty, Haenel licensed the manufacture of their SMGs outside Germany, granting manufacturing rights to the Pieper Company in Belgium and Schweizerische Industrie Gesellschaft (SIG) in Switzerland. Pieper manufactured unmarked MP 28.II guns (see below) for sale by Haenel. SIG-made guns were produced in several calibres, and with various minor manufacturing changes. These were usually referred to as the 'Bergmann'. Many of these SIG-manufactured guns (as well as the Pieper MP 28.II) would be purchased by the Japanese military forces and redesignated as the Type BE.

The MP 28.II

The MP 28.II was essentially an improved version of the MP 18.I. Most models of the MP 28.II were furnished with a lever that permitted a choice of semi- or full-automatic fire. For semi-automatic fire, these models had a disconnector that automatically released the trigger sear to catch the bolt in the rear position after each shot.

As noted, the Belgian Pieper firm produced the MP 28.II under licence from Haenel, in several minor variations, for sale to police and military forces in Belgium, the Netherlands, Japan, China, South America and elsewhere throughout the world. Many of the Pieper-made MP 28.II weapons, probably meant for commercial sale through Haenel, are not

German military personnel during the Warsaw ghetto uprising of 1943. The soldier in the foreground is armed with an MP 28.II. (Cody Images)

marked with a designation or place of manufacture. The Belgian Army adopted the weapon in 1934 under the designation MI 34 (Mitraillette Modele 34) and it was also known as the 'Schmeisser Bayard'. Guns manufactured for the Belgian Army are marked 'Anciens Etablissements Pieper SA Herstal Belgique' on the left side of the receiver.

Vollmer's first designs

Another firearms engineer and designer working on similar SMG designs during the same period was Heinrich Vollmer (1885–1961) of Vollmer Werke Maschinenfabrik. Design of full-automatic weapons attracted him so much that in 1925 – putting aside his earlier profession, the manufacture of wood-cutting tools – he designed his own kind of SMG, the VMP 1925. The 9mm VMP 1925 featured a 25-round, bottom-mounted drum magazine and a vertical foregrip. He offered the gun to the German Army, after which the trials recommended further development. In addition to SMGs he was also involved in developing light machine guns (LMGs).

The VMP 1925 design took time and resulted in a limited number of prototypes, but none reached a full development stage. This weapon came to be known as the MG Vollmer, and later also as the VMG 1927. In 1927 Vollmer obtained a patent covering the breech mechanism of the weapon. It operated on the principle of short recoil with a rotary locking mechanism for the bolt, carried by helical grooves, and was fed from a small drum magazine underneath the receiver. It consisted of only 78 parts while the standard machine gun of those days, the MG 08/15, consisted of 383 parts. Even later on, Vollmer offered his design in cooperation with Mauser Werke as the MauserVollmer 1931 (MV 31) to the German ordnance board, the Inspektion für Waffen und Gerät (IWG). This machine gun was quite a simple and decent design, featuring a quick-change barrel and a drum magazine, but after thorough testing it was not adopted by the German forces.

Following the 1938 *Anschluss* between Germany and Austria, the German Army acquired most of the available MP 30s and MP 34s (in Austrian issue, these were chambered for the standard Austrian 9×23mm Steyr pistol round). A number were then re-barrelled to chamber 9×19mm ammunition and issued to German troops as the MP 34(ö) – Maschinenpistole 34 österreichisch. Many MP 34s were issued to SS troops and other Nazi paramilitary formations, as seen with this officer of the Reichsarbeitsdienst (RAD; Reich Labour Service). (AdeQ Historical Archives)

In 1930, Vollmer introduced an improved design; this resulted in the VMP 1930, which utilized his patented telescopic guide of the recoil (main) spring, and included a side-feed mechanism using box magazines. He produced and sold small amounts of this SMG, but it was not enough to keep his kind of enterprise economically viable. Therefore on 20 October 1931 he sold the entire design, including the patent rights, to the Erfurter Maschinenfabrik (ERMA) headed by Berthold Geipel (1888–1971).

The EMP

ERMA produced the Vollmer design in a variety of models under one common name – EMP (ERMA Maschinenpistole). These weapons differed in barrel length, type of sights, safety arrangements and availability of accessories, but the general layout and features were the same. Wooden-stocked, the EMP fed from a double-row box magazine situated on the left and ejected spent casings to the right. The weapon could be rapidly disassembled using a catch situated behind the trigger guard; this novel design element could prove lethal to the shooter if the catch was hit accidentally while firing the EMP (worldguns.ru).

This German soldier on the Eastern Front is armed with an EMP. As well as seeing service with Axis forces and others during World War II, EMPs were sold to France, Spain and several South American countries. (Cody Images)

Offering select-fire capability, the EMP was blowback-operated and fired from an open bolt. In such firearms the bolt is held to the rear. When the trigger is pulled the bolt goes forward, feeding a round from the magazine into the chamber and firing it. The action is cycled by the energy of the shot; this sends the bolt back to the rear, ejecting the empty cartridge case and preparing for the next shot. The main spring was protected from foreign objects like mud and stones by the telescopic tube in which it was housed. It was the EMP's telescopic cylinder return-spring guide that would play a future role in the development of the subsequent MP 36 and later models.

The MK 36.III and MP 36

After the assumption of power in Germany by the German National Socialist Workers' Party and Hitler's renunciation of the Versailles Treaty in 1935, the new Third Reich began to rebuild the German armed forces. The SMG became the subject of considerable attention in the German military. Various Bergmann and Solothurn models were used, but not officially adopted, by certain Heer (Army) and SS units. Then Haenel developed the MK 36.III and ERMA built a prototype known variously as the EMP 36 and the MP 36; the latter designation is used here to distinguish it from the earlier EMP.

The MP 36 was developed independently by ERMA's Berthold Geipel, with funding from the German Army. Taking design elements from Vollmer's VMP 1930 and EMP, it offered select-fire capability, with a fire-mode selector located above the trigger housing. All of the metal components of the MP 36 were manufactured from machined-steel stock; it used wooden furniture instead of the plastic later used on the MP 38 and MP 40 (the pistol-grip panels were of chequered wood). The folding metal stock of the MP 36 was very similar to that of the later designs, but there were no springs, detents or release buttons; it folded and extended under the friction of the snug-fitting parts and the butt plate had machined grooves instead of being smooth like those found on the MP 40. The front sling-swivel was easily rotated to either side. Magazine catch was a latch type similar to those used in earlier designs, rather than the button release that would be a feature of the MP 38. A magazine-release lever was located at the rear of the housing.

The bolt assembly of the MP 36 bore a similarity with the later MP 38, but with the exception that the front portion of the MP 36 bolt was a separate piece and a locking screw was attached. In terms of sights, the front sight was an unprotected design while the rear sight was similar to that of the MP 38. The MP 36 was devoid of any identification markings except for the underside of the wooden foregrip and serial numbers on various parts. This area was marked in a circular pattern 'EMP/ERMA ERFURT/36'.

The cocking handle of the MP 36 was located on the receiver's left side; it appears to have been the very first German weapon to have this feature in such a position. The reasoning behind the left-side cocking handle was that it allowed the user's hand to remain on the pistol grip with his finger near the trigger, allowing him to cock the weapon easily with his other hand. In addition, it was thought that this layout would make for a more rapid magazine change during combat. The knob was similar to that used on the earlier ERMA weapons such as the EMP 35. The unique magazine housing was slightly canted approximately 30 degrees to the left. Magazines were not interchangeable with those later developed for the MP 38 and MP 40; when an MP 36 was captured from Reichsmarschall Hermann Göring's Karinhall estate there was no magazine in it and an MP 38 magazine had to be adapted to fit. The MP 36 field-stripping procedures were very similar to those of the MP 38, however.

The MP 36 was for many years virtually unknown, due to the extreme rarity of surviving weapons. There are two examples known to exist: serial number 001 is in the possession of a military museum in Prague in the Czech Republic, while serial number 014, believed to have once been part of Reichsmarschall Göring's collection, is in a private collection in the United States.

Here a Luftwaffe soldier carries an MP 34(ö) alongside a colleague armed with an MP 38 or MP 40. (Cody Images)

THE MP 38

Initial development

In 1937, the Heereswaffenamt (Army Ordnance Office) decided to use the Schmeisser system, and not the Vollmer system as used in the EMP or MP 36. Vollmer then worked on Geipel's MP 36 and in 1938 submitted a prototype to answer the Heereswaffenamt's request for a new SMG, which would be adopted as the MP 38. The ERMA plant, the only facility that produced the MP 38, manufactured this model from 1938 through to 1940. The Wehrmacht (German Armed Forces) initially adopted the MP 38 in about August 1938. In 1939, the Heer officially adopted the MP 38 for use by armoured forces and airborne units; it was only the second SMG to be adopted officially by the Heer. Designed by ERMA, this new SMG was destined to have as great an effect on SMG design as had the MP 18.I.

A German enlisted soldier with an MP 38. Of interest are his early slab-sided magazine and canvas magazine pouch. (AdeQ Historical Archives)

An MP 38, distinguished by its ribbed receiver tube and cut-out hold in the magazine well. (AdeQ Historical Archives)

Since the development of the MP 18.I by Schmeisser there had been very little change in bolt design; the bolt used in the MP 38 and MP 40 was clearly an offspring of the patented Schmeisser-designed bolt. Essentially a simplification of the MP 36, the MP 38 offered several advantages over other SMGs of the period before World War II, such as the MP 18.I and MP 28.II. The receiver was made of machined-steel stock, rather than being fabricated by sheet-steel stamping methods, and the gun was constructed entirely of metal and plastic, omitting the heavy wooden stocks present on other SMGs at that time. The stock, of formed-steel construction, folded under the gun when not in use – making it the first important SMG to use a folding stock. With the stock folded, the overall length of the gun was shortened by 20.3cm. This proved to be a key advantage, as most SMGs at the time were on fixed wooden stocks; it meant the MP 38 could easily be racked up in tanks and armoured vehicles, or conveniently carried into combat by parachute troops. An aluminium bar mounted beneath the barrel served as a barrel rest or protector for firing the gun from the port of an armoured vehicle. The front sight was fixed and the rear sight consisted of a square-notch double leaf adjustable for 100m and 200m. The MP 38's markings appeared on the recoil housing at the rear of the receiver.

MP 38 variants

ERMA continued experimenting in order to improve the MP 38. A lightweight version, of which there are three known examples (one of which is in Prague's Military Museum), was developed between late 1939 and early 1940. Designated as the MP 38(L), it was of a different construction in that it was made from cast-aluminium parts. It weighed 1kg less than an average MP 38, and was probably intended for airborne troops or for those infantrymen usually weighed down by other equipment. This experimental weapon featured a one-piece receiver and magazine-housing assembly. In addition, the trigger housing, grip frame and foregrip assembly formed one piece (de Vries & Martens 2001: 20). The bakelite foregrip was deleted and the pistol grips were of wood, simplifying its appearance and construction. However, sheet-metal construction proved to be cheaper, easier and faster for manufacturers, and eventually led to the introduction of the next generation of SMGs.

These weapons were stamped with the following markings: 'MP 38 (L)', 'WaA280', 'EE', and a firing proof mark consisting of an eagle and swastika. The Heereswaffenamt marking was an inspection stamp used for ERMA parts from 1935 to 1942. The 'L' designation could stand for 'Leicht' (light) or 'Leichtmetall' (light metal), but to date no documentation on these experimental guns has come to light. Missing was the standard '27' code commonly found on ERMA-made weapons of the time.

A serious problem associated with the open-bolt system of the MP 38 was its safety or lack thereof. When the bolt was jarred out of the sear it would slam forward and fire the gun. The fitting of a positive bolt lock in the form of a lock on the bolt handle, which was then fitted into a notch in the receiver, apparently fixed the problem. This simple modification to the MP 38 was then utilized by German ordnance workshops with parts supplied by ERMA. These improvements led to further modifications, and to the development of the next version of this iconic SMG – the MP 40.

THE MP 40

The chief difference between the MP 38 and MP 40 was that the latter was designed for fast, simplified and consequently less expensive mass production. The MP 40 benefited from certain cost-saving alterations, notably in the more extensive use of stamped-steel rather than machined parts. Producing a milled receiver and its components results in a lot of wasted steel; it costs more in terms of machine time, as well as making the weapon a bit heavier. In comparison a stamped-steel construction takes less time and minimizes the amount of waste in milling steel components – from an accountant's viewpoint it is also less costly. The marking 'MP 40' appeared on the recoil housing at the rear of the receiver.

9mm MP 40, fourth production variant

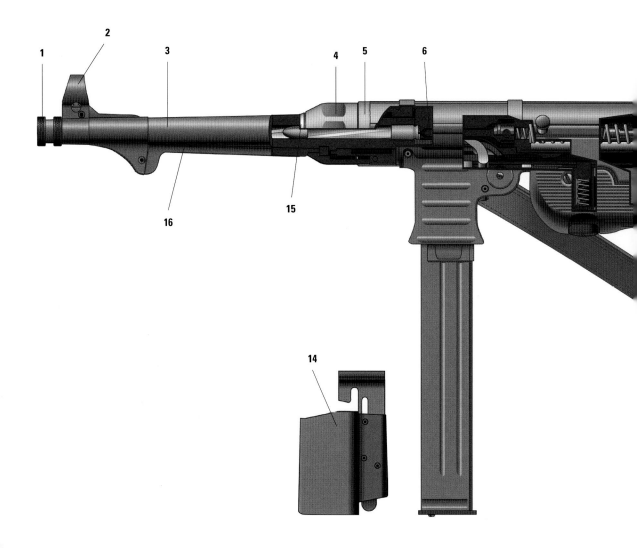

1.	Barrel cap	11.	Stock pivot	21.	Recoil guide
2.	Front sight	12.	Pistol grip	22.	Rear sight
3.	Barrel	13.	Sling	23.	Buffer spring
4.	Barrel nut	14.	Reloading device	24.	Buffer housing
5.	Collar	15.	Barrel nut washer	25.	Trigger guard
6.	Firing pin	16.	Resting bar	26.	Sear lever
7.	Stock arm	17.	Bolt	27.	Receiver lock
8.	Shoulder piece	18.	Recoil spring	28.	Magazine release
9.	Shoulder piece pivot	19.	Bolt handle	29.	Magazine guide
10.	Winter trigger	20.	Chamber cover	30.	Magazine

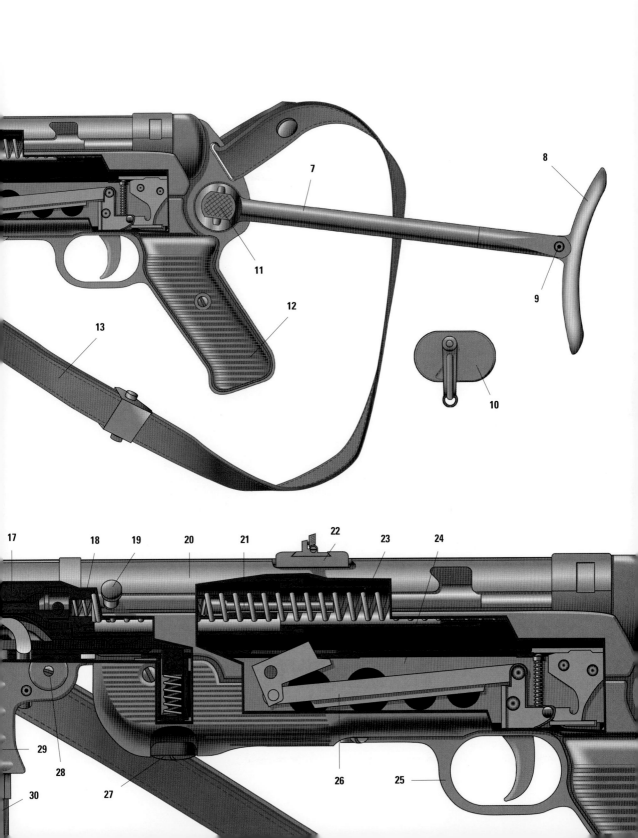

7

8

9

11

12

13

10

17 18 19 20 21 22 23 24

29

28

27

30

26 25

Wartime improvements

There were various manufacturing variations of the MP 40 that continued during the war, and distinguished it from the MP 38. In 1942 the cocking handle was changed from a simple hook-style handle to an improved type, which included a latch that allowed the bolt to be locked in the forward position. A circular notch was cut into the receiver to lock the bolt handle in the forward position. Those examples of the MP 38 that featured the new bolt handle and modified receiver were unofficially referred to as the MP 38/40 model – by May 1943 most MP 38s and previously produced MP 40s had been upgraded with these new safety bolts. All parts were to be obtained from the Wehrmacht supply depot in Kassel. In the same year (1942), the barrel-rest bar was changed from aluminium to plastic.

In many cases variations were outwardly unnoticeable, and it was only when the weapon was disassembled that these differences became apparent. The modifications reflected gradual production improvements since the adoption of the MP 38. One case in point is provided by the development of four different types of grip section for the MP 38 and MP 40. The first type, an aluminium grip featuring three round holes and one square hole, was produced between 1938 and 1941 for the MP 38 by ERMA and Haenel. The second type was a simplified sheet-metal 'open' or 'hollow' grip with a ridge around the trigger guard; this was produced by Steyr, ERMA, Haenel, Merz Werke and National Krupp Registrier Kassen from 1939 until 1944. A third type, produced by Steyr in 1942–43, was a further-simplified sheet-metal construction consisting of a one-piece grip with two small oblong holes and one round hole; it was slightly

This group of Waffen-SS personnel aboard a captured T-34 includes two men armed with MP 40s. (Cody Images)

thicker and there was no ridge around the trigger guard. Finally, the fourth type was further simplified again: the grip (with a single round hole for the grip screw) was permanently welded together with the lower receiver, a metal band was welded all over the grip, trigger guard and the back end of the receiver, and the ridge encircling the trigger guard was restored.

Between 1940 and 1945 there were five variant production versions of the MP 40, each with its own characteristics; in their excellent study of the MP 38, MP 40 and MP 41, Guus de Vries and Bas Martens spell out the key differences between the versions (de Vries & Martens 2001: 24–33). The first element that reveals the production version is the magazine housing; this was smooth sheet metal for the first version, but ribbed sheet metal for the other four variants. The grip and trigger guard

Manufacturers and their markings

There were three major manufacturers of the MP 38, MP 40 and MP 41. ERMA Waffenfabrik ('ayf'), based in Erfurt, manufactured the MP 38 from 1938 to 1940 before switching to the manufacture of the MP 40; production ended in 1945. Steyr-Daimler-Puch ('bnz'), based in Steyr, was the second firm to manufacture the MP 40, and was responsible for the highest production numbers during the time the weapon was produced. Production ran from 1940 to 1945. C.G. Haenel Waffen- und Fahrradfabrik ('fxo'), based in Suhl, produced the MP 41 at some point in 1941–42; the firm also manufactured MP 40 parts from 1942 to 1945 as a subcontractor for ERMA.

The three letters following the names of the manufacturers were code letters assigned between 1934 and 1945. All MP 38 and MP 40 weapons were marked with these code letters. They were stamped on top of the buffer housing to the rear of the receiver. The year of manufacture was stamped on the buffer housing just below the manufacturer's code letters ('42', for example, indicated that the gun was made in 1942). Some parts for the MP 40 were furnished by subcontractors, and bore their code letters as well. For example, 'cos' indicated Merzwerke Gebr. of Frankfurt am Main, and 'cnd' was National Krupp Registrier Kassen of Berlin.

A logo or stamp for the companies that were involved in the production of bakelite was developed by the Materialprüfungsamt (Material Proofing House) from Berlin Dalhem in December 1938. The bakelite grip plates and the foregrip were produced by two suppliers: Vereinigte Isolatorenwerke AG/Viacowerke ('gbm') based at Berlin-Pankow, and Allgemeine Elektrizitätsgesellschaft (AEG/Elektrolux) at Henningsdorf. The handgrips produced by AEG had a small '38' code in the logo, while those made by Vereinigte Isolatorenwerke AG/ Viacowerke were designated by a stamp with the 'gbm' code. A variety of colours and styles were made by these manufacturers during the course of the war.

ABOVE A close-up of the mould manufacturer's markings found inside the bakelite foregrip of the MP 40. This handgrip was produced by AEG, which had a small '38' code in the logo. (AdeQ Historical Archives)

also provide clues about the production variant. While the first, second and third versions had a sheet-metal grip and trigger guard comprising two halves that were stamped together, the fourth and fifth versions had a single-piece grip and trigger guard, with the trigger guard being thicker and (for the fifth variant) ridged. The fifth variant's grip and trigger guard were further distinguished by being welded to the lower receiver (de Vries & Martens 2001: 33). The retracting handle was in one piece for the first and second variants, but many of these original handles were replaced by the later two-piece version used for the third, fourth and fifth variants. The third production variant was further distinguished by differences in the barrel nut, barrel bar and barrel bushing (de Vries & Martens 2001: 29), while the fourth variant appears to have been built by Steyr only.

Modified MP 40s

As the war progressed, the Germans experimented with a modified MP 40 that handled two side-by-side 32-round magazines. The MP 40/I (sometimes mistakenly referred to as the MP 40/II) was tested in 1942. This version of the MP 40 had a dual magazine well that slid horizontally to use the additional magazine when the first became empty. If successful this MP 40 variant would have provided the user with a total of 64 rounds available for immediate use.

This design was intended to counter the superior firepower of the Soviet PPSh-41, but made the weapon heavy and unbalanced in the field, and did not work well. The magazine housing jammed easily and was vulnerable to fouling (worldguns.ru). Only very limited numbers were made of this experimental weapon. Tellingly, by 1943 the Soviets had

Most markings on the MP 38 and MP 40 are found on the recoil housing at the rear of the upper receiver. In this case the markings for the MP 41 are found on the top of the receiver behind the ejection port. (AdeQ Historical Archives)

shifted the production of PPSh-41 drums to 35-round magazines due to combat malfunctions.

The Germans experimented with the MP 40 or components thereof in combination with other systems. The double-feed system of the MP 40/I continued to be tested in other developments during the war. Testing of the EMP 44 began in 1942 and featured the same dual-feeding system that utilized the MP 40 magazine. The prototype was intended for use in armoured vehicles and fortifications. After only a few prototypes being built the testing was halted and the remaining dual-feeding system was transferred to a small number of MP 40s.

This MP 40, with the characteristic ribbed magazine well and semi-smooth receiver tube, was made by Steyr in 1942. (AdeQ Historical Archives)

THE MP 41

A variant of the MP 40, the MP 41, was designed by Louis Schmeisser and produced in very limited numbers by the C.G. Haenel plant in 1941. The MP 41's fire selector was similar to that found on the MP 36. This model was intended for carbine use, and was therefore equipped with a standard wooden stock rather than the folding stock of the MP 40. The MP 41 had a selector switch for full- or semi-automatic fire, unlike the MP 38 and MP 40.

Because the Heereswaffenamt did not adopt the MP 41, the Haenel firm stopped production very quickly, and began instead to manufacture parts for the MP 40 as a subcontractor. In addition, the shortness of the MP 41's production run was due in part to ERMA's filing of a successful patent-infringement lawsuit against Schmeisser's employer, Haenel. The limited numbers of the MP 41 went to SD (Sicherheitsdienst, the SS intelligence agency) and SS troops and German police units, as well as to the troops of Germany's ally, Romania, because standardization of weapons in these units was not as important as for regular front-line combat forces.

AMMUNITION

The Parabellum cartridge

The MP 38, MP 40 and MP 41 all fired the Parabellum 9×19mm cartridge. The average soldier armed with an MP 40 was expected to be equipped with six loaded magazines of 32 rounds each, thereby carrying a total of 192 rounds. However, due to feeding issues the experienced shooter usually loaded no more than 28 rounds per magazine, giving a total of 168 rounds. Oberkommando der Wehrmacht (OKW; Supreme Command of the Armed Forces) specified that for combat units in the field, there should be sufficient ammunition available for a 48-hour period; in 1941, OKW calculated this allowance to be 768 rounds per MP 40. The 9mm cartridges were packed in boxes of 16 cartridges, each box having a blue label designating the calibre of the cartridges it contained. Fifty-two of these boxes were packed into a carton and five cartons were packed into a case that held a total of 4,160 rounds and weighed approximately 58kg.

The Parabellum cartridge was designed by Georg Luger and introduced in 1902 by DWM for their Luger semi-automatic pistol. The initial cartridge was created by removing the bottleneck of the 7.65mm Luger cartridge, resulting in a rimless cartridge; therefore the 9mm round was a rimless cartridge with a straight case. The jacketed bullet weighed approximately 7.5g (115 grains) and produced a muzzle velocity of 390m/sec. The point (ogive) of the bullet was slightly redesigned in the second decade of the 20th century in order to improve feeding. After World War I, acceptance of this calibre increased, and 9mm pistols and SMGs were adopted by military and police users in a number of countries – primarily due to the availability of compact pistols offering a large magazine capacity that used this cartridge.

Ammunition types

A variety of ammunition types were used with the MP 40, each with a special purpose. Guus de Vries and Bas Martens provide a valuable survey of the various cartridges used for the MP 38, MP 40 and MP 41 (de Vries & Martens 2001: 46). At the outbreak of World War II the 9mm round had a brass case marked with a star on the base. In 1939–40, a steel case with corrosion-resistant copper or brass finish was introduced as a means of conserving brass supplies. From 1941, the finish of the cartridge was changed to a green-tinted lacquer; black lacquer was used to seal the cartridge's primer as means of preventing contamination from lubrication oil.

The various 9mm Parabellum cartridges were given the German military designation of 'Pistolenpatrone 08' (Pistol Cartridge 08), usually combined with a descriptive term to give the round a specific designation. The Pistolenpatrone 08 was the standard ball cartridge that contained a nickel- or copper-jacketed lead-core bullet. The Pistolenpatrone 08 für Tropen (for the Tropics), a ball cartridge for tropical use, was treated to prevent moisture from reaching the propellant inside by sealing the primer with lacquer and sealing the bullet to the cartridge case; seal and primer were usually annulus black and later red.

To conserve lead during wartime, the lead core of the bullet was replaced by an iron core encased with lead. This bullet, identified by a black bullet jacket, was a standard ball cartridge; it was designated as the 08 mE (*mit Eisenkern* – 'with iron core'). By 1944, the black jacket of the 08 mE bullet was dispensed with, and these bullets were produced with normal copper-coloured jackets. The Pistolenpatrone 08 mit Eisenkern für Tropen was a steel-core bullet with a sealed case-mouth for tropical climates. Another wartime variation,

The 9mm Parabellum cartridge was the standard round used for the MP 38, MP 40 and MP 41. Seen here is a wartime-issued box of 9mm ammunition, together with a standard magazine loader that is appropriately marked 'MP 38u.40' and an MP 40 magazine. (AdeQ Historical Archives)

manufactured from 1942, was designated the 08 sE bullet (*Sintereisen* – 'sintered iron') and identified by its dark-grey jacket; it was created by compressing iron powder at high temperature into a solid material. A tropical version of the cartridge with sintered bullet, the Pistolenpatrone 08 Sintereisen für Tropen, was also manufactured.

There were several cartridges for special use. The Nahpatrone 08 was a subsonic round commonly used with silencers; this ball cartridge's load was reduced and the cartridge was sometimes fitted with a heavier bullet. Some of these cartridges were found to have a headstamp consisting only of the letter 'X'; cases containing these rounds were marked in light green. Very small quantities of a poisonous cartridge, inspired by those captured from the Soviets and designated as the Kampfstoffpatrone 08, were manufactured in 1944. The Germans also experimented with an explosive cartridge, the Sprengpatrone 08, which contained a bullet loaded with a pellet of lead azide. The Beschusspatrone 08 was a test cartridge that developed approximately 75 per cent more pressure than usual; those cartridges with a green-lacquered case-head, a green primer annulus and a headstamp marked 'BESCHUSS' are some of the variants encountered.

For training, several cartridges are known to have been used with the MP 40. The Platzpatrone 08 was a blank cartridge used for training and exercises. There were several variations of the metal dummy cartridge known as the Exerzierpatrone 08, lacking primer and propellant and having the bullet being fixed to the case; the types encountered include dummy cartridges partly nickel-plated with holes, partly nickel-plated without holes, completely nickel-plated without holes, and completely nickel-plated with holes. The Exerzierpatrone 08 Kunststoff was a red- or black-coloured plastic dummy cartridge that was adopted around 1940; the round was a one-piece plastic cartridge with a steel case-bottom.

Headstamp markings on the 9mm Parabellum cartridge were usually placed in four positions. At the 12 o'clock position on the cartridge base was the manufacturer's code; initially this code consisted of the letter 'P' with a number, later followed by a two- or three-letter code. The manufacturer's lot was marked at the 6 o'clock position, while the case material was located at the 3 o'clock position. The year of manufacture was located at the 9 o'clock position. The '+' symbol indicated that it was a strengthened case, and a steel case was marked with 'St' or 'St+' (de Vries & Martens 2001: 44).

ACCESSORIES

Magazines: types and variations

There were six types of magazines: MP 38 – 0 (slab-sided); MP 38 – A (after-ribbed); MP 38u.40 – 0 (slab-sided); MP 38u.40 – A (after-ribbed); MP 38u.40 – B (ribbed); MP 41 – B (ribbed). It was observed that the early Type 0 magazines were susceptible to dirt and grime building up, and so from March 1942 all newly manufactured magazines – the Type B variants – were required to be ribbed, a process carried out by Haenel. The rationale for this was that the dirt and grime would collect in the recessed areas of the ribbed magazines, reducing the likelihood of a jam.

MP 38 and MP 40 magazines could also be used with other weapons. A small quantity of MP 38u.40 magazines were modified by German forces during World War II for use with the Finnish Suomi M31 SMG. Germany ordered approximately 3,042 M31 Suomi SMGs from Finland during World War II; also, 120 Suomi SMGs were presented to the German troops of AOK Norwegen (Army Norway) in 1942 for use on the Finnish Front. Most of these weapons left Finland with German troops in 1944 and were subsequently used in other theatres of the war. Since magazine production in Germany was geared up for MP 38u.40 magazines, it was simpler to weld an adapter to the rear of the existing magazines than to initiate production of another type of magazine altogether.

An overview of the various styles of magazines encountered for the MP 38, MP 40 and MP 41. (AdeQ Historical Archives)

Another weapon adapted for use with the MP 40 magazine was the Soviet PPSh-41. Many of these were captured by the Germans and used against their former owners. The Wehrmacht designated this SMG the MP 717(r); a number of these were converted to use the standard 9mm cartridge, by changing the barrel and adding a magazine adapter into the magazine well in order to use an MP 40 stick magazine. The original bolt of the PPSh-41 was retained without any modifications, because the 9mm Parabellum and the Soviet 7.62×25mm cartridge shared similar base dimensions.

A close-up of markings typically found for the MP 38/MP 40 and for the MP 41. Since the MP 41 was never adopted by the Wehrmacht it wasn't subject to Waffenamt markings and other military restrictions, thereby being free in placing its factory name and logo ('HAENEL' within an arrow). (AdeQ Historical Archives)

Magazine loaders

Like the MP 38 itself, the initial design of the magazine loader appeared in 1938. It can be distinguished from later variants by its smooth finish and by the fact that the first variant's push-down button was welded to the bar that pushed the cartridges into the magazine, rather than being all one piece (www.mp40.nl). At first only Haenel produced the magazine loader, but from 1940 seven more manufacturers were also involved: Steyr-Daimler-Puch AG, Werk Steyr; Eisenwerke G. Meurer GmbH, Tetschen/Elbe (Decin); ERMA, Erfurt; Carl Ullrich & Co. Metallwaren, Oberschönau, bei Zella Mehlis; Frankische Eisenwerke, AG Niederscheld/Dillkreis; Loch & Hartenberger, Metalwarenfabrik; and Steyr-Daimler-Puch AG, Werk Graz, Fuhrhoffsgasse 44 (www.mp40.nl).

Between 1938 and 1940 the loaders were not marked with a designation. Beginning in 1940 the loaders were designated 'MP 38u.40' and bore the marks of the various makers' codes and Waffenamts, as well as the year of manufacture (from 1942 on) with some loaders. The only exceptions were those loaders made for the MP 41, which were marked 'MP41' with the 'Haenel' arrow commercial logo.

Filling the magazine with the loader was a simple operation. The magazine loader was placed around the magazine with the back to the left, until it locked; then with the magazine vertically in place it was ready to be loaded. With his left hand the soldier operated the push-down button of the loader downwards to the stop. With his right hand he put the cartridge (single), case head towards the left, under the magazine lips and pushed it to the left into the magazine when at the same time it released

Late in the war Germany's ally, Finland, began supplying the Suomi M31 SMG to the Wehrmacht. A small quantity of German MP 38u.40 magazines were modified by the German forces during World War II for use with the M31. Since magazine production in Germany was geared up for MP 38u.40 magazines, it was simpler to weld an adapter to the rear of existing magazines than to initiate production of another type of magazine altogether. From left to right one can compare the differences between a standard MP 40 magazine, an adapted one, and the original unaltered Finnish version. (AdeQ Historical Archives)

27

German infantrymen cleaning their weapons and sidearms, including a P 08 Luger, a Kar 98k rifle, a bayonet and an MP 38. Note the distinctive ribbing on the SMG's receiver. (AdeQ Historical Archives)

the pressure of the push-button. When 32 cartridges were filled, the bottom cartridge became visible through a hole at the back of the magazine. Overfilling led to malfunctions and stoppages. Usually, to prevent problems in the function of the weapon, up to 28 rounds were loaded at a time, thereby relieving stress on the magazine spring.

After the end of World War II, both Norway and Bulgaria developed their own magazine loaders for the MP 38s and MP 40s fielded by their military and law-enforcement personnel. Present-day sporting shooters have found that the Vigneron magazine loader developed by the Belgian company Précision Liégoise SA for its Vigneron SMG works well for the MP 38 and MP 40, too (www.mp40.nl).

Found along with the loader in a magazine pouch was the magazine-cleaning brush (Reinigungsbürste für Magazin MP). The rectangle-shaped cleaning brush was used to clean the magazine housing once it was taken apart by removing the base plate, spring and follower (www.mp40.nl).

A variety of materials and styles were used in making pouches for MP 38, MP 40 and MP 41 magazines. Depicted here are the three basic styles encountered, from left to right: early leather magazine pouch; leather-and-canvas magazine-pouch variant; and the common canvas magazine pouch used throughout the war. (AdeQ Historical Archives)

Magazine pouches

The subject of magazine pouches is a book unto itself because of all the variations and styles that existed during and even after World War II. The standard magazine pouch set consisted of two three-pocket pouches of which the left pouch contained a compartment for the magazine loader and magazine-cleaning brush. Each pouch was normally fitted with belt loops and a D-ring. These magazine pouches were constructed of various materials and in different colours, such as leather, blue-grey canvas, field-grey cloth, dark-green canvas, field-grey canvas and beige canvas. The closure fittings were made of leather or metal-tipped cloth straps.

Another style of pouch encountered was one that had provision for six magazines and a magazine loader. This was fitted with a carrying strap. Early manuals described this as the pouch for the MP 38. There were also a variety of six-pocket magazine pouches manufactured during the war (de Vries & Martens 2001: 42).

In *Die Maschinenpistole 40: Beschreibung und Handhabung*, Heinz Denckler specified the following basic rules: sand and dirt should be removed from the inside and outside of the magazine pouches; the magazines should always be placed with the opening toward the bottom in the magazine pouch; the magazine pouches are to be closed after pulling out or inserting the magazines; and during each pause in combat, the user should inspect the weapon, the magazine and the magazine pouches.

This soldier is seen with a pair of canvas MP 40 magazine pouches. Of interest is that the fastening straps are made of canvas instead of leather; metal tips have been added in order to act as a follower when fastening the pouches. (AdeQ Historical Archives)

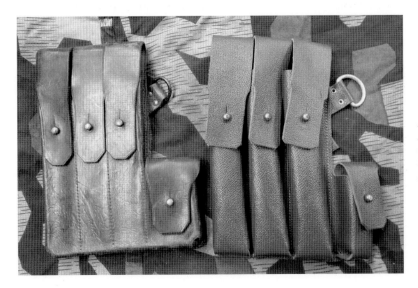

After the war the Norwegian Army continued to use German equipment, such as the German Stahlhelm helmet and MP 38s and MP 40s, well into the late 1980s. Seen here are early (brown leather; left) and later (green leather; right) versions of the magazine pouches made for users of the MP 40 serving in the Norwegian Army. (AdeQ Historical Archives)

These non-commissioned officers are carrying an early slab-sided MP 40 (left) and a standardized rib-sided MP 40 (right). This photo is an excellent study of how the leather slings have been attached to these weapons. (AdeQ Historical Archives)

Carrying slings

According to the manuals, the MP 40 was to be carried by one of two means: either it was hung behind the right shoulder, muzzle up, or it could also be hung in front of the body, across the chest. Carrying the MP 40 with the muzzle down or pointing forward was discouraged. This was to instil proper weapon handling as well as to ensure that the weapon was pointed in a safe direction when not in use, in case of accidental discharge.

The MP 40 sling, constructed from tanned leather, measured approximately 2.5cm wide and was roughly 1.2m in total length – shorter than that of the Kar 98k. On one end of the sling, there were two attachment holes with a metal stud that provided for modest adjustment. On the other end of the sling there was a metallic clasping device that was used to secure the sling at the butt end of the firearm. There was also a leather cinch strap included with the sling. The ends of the sling were usually impressed or ink-stamped with the Waffenamt eagles and a manufacturer's code.

Muzzle covers

Originally the muzzle cover designed for the MP 38 (Mündungsschoner für MP 38) was of tooled-steel and sheet-metal construction. Intended to prevent dirt from entering the barrel, it measured roughly 38mm long, 38mm tall and 22mm wide, and featured a brazed-on, raised, forward sight guard and a spring-loaded, circular, flip-up muzzle cap. This muzzle cover slipped on to the end of the MP 38 barrel and was turned to position the sight guard over the forward sight. The muzzle cover was marked with a stamped Waffenamt (WaA 101) and what appears to be a manufacturer's initial or logo of C. Bettenmüller & Cie., C., GmbH., Metalwarenfabrik, Bretten/Baden, Germany.

The early muzzle cap cover for the MP 38, shown with the smaller muzzle cap cover of the Kar 98k (left), the standard-issue bolt-action rifle in German service. (AdeQ Historical Archives)

The designers' fates

At the end of World War II, the victors began gathering up materials and documents relating to German weapons production, and even appropriating the people who had developed innovative firearms designs. Among those taken as 'spoils of war' was Hugo Schmeisser. On 3 April 1945 American troops began to occupy the city of Suhl. Weapons manufacturing was completely prohibited during this time. Hugo Schmeisser and his brother Hans were interrogated for weeks by teams of weapons experts working for the American and British secret services. At the end of June 1945, American troops evacuated Suhl and all of Thuringia. One month later, the Soviets assumed control over the area, starting a civilian works project to manufacture weapons for the USSR. By August 1945, the Soviets had created 50 StG 44s from existing assembly parts, and had begun inspecting their design. In all, 10,785 sheets of technical designs were confiscated as part of their research. In October 1945, Schmeisser was forced to work for the Red Army and instructed to continue development of new weapons.

Schmeisser's brilliance continued to impress the Red Army, and he, along with other weapons designers and their families, was relocated to the USSR. On 24 October 1946 the German specialists rode a train to Izhevsk in the southern Ural Mountains, where a centre of Soviet firearms development

was located. There Mikhail Kalashnikov worked as general designer of small arms for the Red Army, his design subordinates including Schmeisser, designer of the StG 44, and Werner Gruner of MG 42 fame, who would become a pioneer in sheet-metal embossing technology in the 1950s. Beyond Kalashnikov's 2009 admission that Schmeisser 'helped' design the famous AK-47, which strongly resembled Schmeisser's StG 44, little is known of the German's life during this period. Schmeisser worked in Izhevsk until 1952, when he and other German specialists returned home. At short notice, Schmeisser's stay in the USSR was extended beyond that of the other weapon specialists by half a year. He finally returned home on 9 June 1952. Schmeisser died on 12 September 1953, and was buried in Suhl.

And what about Heinrich Vollmer? After the beginning of World War II Vollmer's activity as a weapon designer had practically ceased. His factory produced small parts for the MP 40, but as a weapon designer Vollmer stepped back. After the war Vollmer and his factory focused on the production of sharpening equipment for wood-cutting tools. Heinrich Vollmer died in 1961 and his company still exists. It recently celebrated its 100th anniversary and is now part of the Vollmer Group, which has its headquarters in Biberach an der Riss, employs 700 people worldwide and turns over more than €100 million a year as of 2013.

This muzzle cap proved impractical as it had to be folded back into the open position before the weapon could be fired – and although most accessories for the MP 38 were interchangeable with the accessories for the MP 40, the steel muzzle covers were not. This design was based on the metal muzzle cap produced for the Kar 98k rifle, but these caps were not interchangeable either. With the introduction of the MP 40, production of the steel muzzle covers was discontinued and they were replaced with rubber muzzle covers, which could be shot off in the case of immediate use, as well as providing protection for the bore.

Blank-firing devices

The blank-firing device (Platzpatronengerät MP) was inserted into the muzzle, and retained by an attaching screw for which the muzzle was threaded. The device constricted the barrel so that sufficient gas pressure from blank cartridges was retained in the barrel to work the action. Post-war versions were also made by the various countries that continued to use the MP 40 after World War II. The Norwegian Army used a white-metal conical-shaped blank-firing adapter for their MP 40s.

The winter trigger for the MP 38 and MP 40 was made by Allweiler AG, Gotthard, Pumpenfabrik, Radolfzell a/Bodensee (wartime code 'ezd'). The contents of the SS-marked frostbite-salve tins also seen here would have been applied to the lips and face, and even small arms, to avoid freezing in the -35°C temperatures of the Russian winter. (AdeQ Historical Archives)

The winter trigger

The winter trigger device (Winterabzug MP) fitted into the trigger guard; a lever extended beneath the device to permit firing the gun with a gloved hand. It was based on the winter trigger made for the Kar 98k, but they were not interchangeable. These were usually marked 'MP' with the manufacturer's code 'ezd'. The code 'ezd' was for Allweiler AG, Gotthard, Pumpenfabrik, Radolfzell a/Bodensee.

Sound suppressors

Two German firms, Arado Flugzeugwerke GmbH, Werk Brandenburg/Havel (hkx), and Adam Schneider AG, Maschinenfabrik, Berlin N 65, Fennstrasse 31 (aod), were instructed by the Heereswaffenamt to develop a sound suppressor for the MP 40. The two firms submitted their examples to the Heereswaffenamt for test and evaluation in February 1943. The Heer found that the suppressors' sound levels were higher than those of comparable Soviet weapons, but their accuracy was better. In addition, the assessors found that the sound suppressors made from rubber baffles did not lead to any degree of success.

Four different sound suppressors were developed for the MP 40: L 41 (original model), L 41 (improved variant), L 42 and L 43. With a diameter of 43mm, a length of 295mm and weight of about 0.7kg, the L 41 (improved variant) suppressor, made by Arado, had a cylindrical shape and was screwed onto the muzzle. The L 42 and L 43 suppressors designed by Schneider were also cylindrical; they were 45mm in diameter, 350mm long and weighed about 0.6kg. The suppressors designed by the two firms required the use of special ammunition: the Nahpatrone (www.mp40.nl).

The Heereswaffenamt had found problems with all four versions of suppressors by January 1945. Use of the L 43 suppressor did not result in any reduction in sound levels. The L 41 suppressor's opening was found to be too small, thereby causing misfires. Worse, the MP 40's threaded muzzle end of the barrel proved to be too short for mounting the Arado suppressors securely. This led to a dangerous misalignment of the suppressor with the barrel, causing the bullet to damage the suppressor as it exited the barrel.

USE
The machine pistol in combat

From the deserts of North Africa to the icy wastes of the Soviet Union, the MP 40 was employed by German troops and their allies in a host of different and often challenging environments. Extremes of temperature, varying humidity and local contaminants – dust, dirt, sand and mud – all took their toll on the weapon. The combination of portability, firepower and reliability offered by the MP 40 endeared the weapon to its users and impressed those who faced it at close quarters.

During the course of World War II the German military recognized three main MPs within their official inventory, as specified in their documents and manuals such as *Vorschrift D 97/Gerätliste* ('Regulation D 97/Equipment List'). These were: Gerätnummer 1-3001 Machinenpistole 38; Gerätnummer 1-3003 Machinenpistole 40; and Gerätnummer 1-3004 Machinenpistole 40/I (the 'MP 40/II' never officially existed in wartime documents).

Members of the Luftwaffe are seen here practising with their MP 38/MP 40s. It appears that some are resting the magazines on the ground to provide a steady support while firing their weapons. (AdeQ Historical Archives)

OPERATING THE MP 40

Before exploring the operational history of the MP 38 and MP 40, we need to be clear about how these weapons were used. German wartime manuals were very specific about how every aspect of the operation of the weapon was to be approached, and they offer key insights into what it was like to use the MP 38 and MP 40.

Loading

The Luftwaffe manual *D (Luft) 5602/Die Ausbildung mit der Maschinenpistole 38 und 40* specified the positions to be adopted while loading the MP 40 when the user was kneeling, standing or prone. When the user was standing, the weapon was to be held with the muzzle diagonally tilted and forward; when the user was kneeling, the weapon was to be supported on the left knee; and in the prone position the weapon had to be slightly turned to the right in order for the magazine to be placed in the magazine well (Iannamico 1999: 10).

During loading, the weapon had to be on 'safe' and then loaded when the tactical situation permitted. Following the correct procedure, the user pulled the bolt handle to the rear until the bolt was caught and held in the cocked position by the sear. Then he could insert a loaded magazine into the magazine well until it clicked into place. The magazine might not be completely inserted if the bolt was closed. The gun was now ready to fire.

This soldier of SS-Panzergrenadier-Division *Das Reich* armed with an MP 40 is pictured during the fighting around Kursk in 1943. (Cody Images)

Loading the MP 40 required the user to develop both familiarity with the gun's weight distribution and some practical tricks for managing its centre of balance. The MP 40 was a very front-heavy gun, partly on account of the lightweight skeleton stock at the rear (which gave little counterbalance), and partly because the full stacked magazine added nearly 0.7kg in weight well towards the front of the weapon. The barrel (typically one of the heaviest parts of a firearm) also added its weight at the front. Gripping the gun with only the right hand on the pistol grip results in the weapon tipping forward, making it difficult to insert and engage the magazine with the left hand. By way of compensation, the German soldier would typically take the weight with the sling around the neck, squeezing the stock of the weapon between right elbow and stomach, this making the weapon more stable.

Firing

The MP 38 and MP 40 both fired full-automatic only, powered by a straightforward blowback action. All models of the MP 40 fired from the open-bolt position. The retracted (i.e. cocked) bolt was held by the trigger sear. Pulling the trigger swung the trigger sear downwards and released the bolt. Under pressure of the recoil spring, the bolt snapped forward and thereby stripped the topmost cartridge out of the magazine and pushed it into the chamber or breech. At the moment the cartridge was completely chambered, the extractor snapped over the base of the cartridge rim and the firing pin (protruding from the bolt) struck the primer, firing the cartridge.

The inertia of the heavy bolt assembly held the cartridge in the chamber until the bullet left the short barrel and chamber pressure dropped to a safe level. The head of the cartridge continued to push back against the bolt until the inertia was overcome. The bolt was then driven to the rear under its own momentum, ejecting the empty cartridge and compressing the operating springs as it approached the rear. The bolt was then driven forward, and the gun continued to fire until the trigger was released, allowing the sear to catch the bolt.

Cyclic rate was 400–550rds/min, depending on the type of ammunition used; the actual deliverable rate of fire, including changes of magazine, was 120–180rds/min. With less recoil and muzzle climb than earlier SMGs such as the MP 18.I, sustained fire resulted in tight bullet placement. Experienced shooters could fire one or two shots at a time by quickly releasing the trigger after each shot.

Effective range was estimated to be 180m, while maximum range was 1,690m. The sight range on the MP 40 went up to 200m (sight folded down) with a lower range of 100m (sight upright). The ammunition's energy at ranges of more than 200m was no longer adequate for a successful engagement. Soldiers were taught that only bursts were fired from the MP 40. The length of bursts depended on the size and distance of the target. In close combat, tightly grouped targets could be easily engaged, with the weapon being swept over the entire width of the target using uninterrupted or traversing fire (Iannamico 1999: 13).

With the folding stock of the MP 40 extended, the shooter had more control over the weapon, allowing him to aim properly and preventing the weapon from rising during firing. This soldier has his magazine resting against the earth while he has his other hand free to add additional support underneath the fore-end. (AdeQ Historical Archives)

The accuracy of the fire was affected by the open-bolt design of the gun. When the trigger was pulled, the bolt was released from its rear position, the sudden shift of mass prior to firing disturbing the balance and therefore the accuracy of the shots. Accuracy was further unsettled by the fact that the cocking handle oscillated rapidly backward and forward, creating a hammer effect that, when combined with a certain degree of muzzle climb, did little for medium-range accuracy. In part, this inaccuracy was part and parcel of the experience for all SMGs; if the soldier wanted pinpoint accuracy, he would use a rifle.

Nevertheless, compared to many SMGs the MP 40 was actually quite accurate. The 9mm Parabellum has very low recoil characteristics, particularly when fired from a gun that weighed 4kg, so the levels of recoil were manageable. Muzzle climb was also balanced, to some degree, by the MP 40s centre of balance being towards the front of the gun. Control of the weapon was further helped by correct posture and grip. The manner of holding the MP 40 while firing was also specified in *D (Luft) 5602/Die Ausbildung mit der Maschinenpistole 38 und 40*. In order to prevent an upwards movement of the muzzle during firing, the weapon in all shooting positions had to be held firmly in both hands with the shoulder stock pulled into the shoulder. Body weight was leaned forward slightly, to compensate for the recoil. In the standing position and with the weapon unsupported, the left hand grasped the magazine well (not the magazine itself). In the prone position, the magazine could be used as a support. Shooting while moving could be done with the shoulder stock folded or extended.

Stoppage procedures

Should the soldier experience a stoppage during firing, he had to let go of the trigger, remove the magazine and pull the bolt back to the furthest position until it was in the safety notch at the rear – thereby rendering it in a safe condition. In case a cartridge or spent shell was in the weapon, it had to be removed. Special attention had to be paid to checking that the chamber was clear; the weapon was still technically 'live' and dangerous if a round was chambered (Iannamico 1999: 6).

Stoppages could be caused by a number of different factors, and their remedies would vary according to the nature of the problem. Common reasons for stoppages included:

(1) Cartridges remaining in the receiver: a spent round was caught between the bolt and chamber (this is commonly called a 'stovepipe'). The probable cause would be a worn or broken extractor. The remedy would be to replace the extractor.

(2) Cartridges not ejected (caught by the bolt): a live round was slammed by the bolt and would not eject. The probable cause would be a worn or broken ejector. The remedy would be to have an armourer replace the ejector.

(3) Bolt in the forward position, live round in chamber: by pulling back the bolt, a live round was ejected. The cause could be a misfire, or the firing pin being broken. The remedy would be to reload and fire again. If the firing pin was broken, then an armourer would have to replace the firing pin or bolt.

(4) Cartridge will not chamber. This could be caused by the magazine being incorrectly filled, dirty or dented. The remedy would be to remove the magazine, pull the bolt back and insert a new magazine (Iannamico 1999: 6).

Operating the safety

To engage the safety, the soldier grasped the weapon with his right hand at the centre of gravity, and with the index finger of the left hand pulled back the bolt handle and placed it in the safety notch. Then, with the left hand, he pushed the magazine into the magazine well until it audibly locked. The weapon was now loaded and on safe. To disengage the safety, with the barrel pointed in the direction of fire, the left hand pulled the bolt handle to the rearmost position and let the bolt, under the pressure of the recoil spring, slide forward, until it was stopped by the trigger sear (Iannamico 1999: 10).

Field-stripping procedures

To field strip the MP 40, the soldier first removed the magazine and placed the bolt in the closed position. He pulled out the receiver-lock button (located on the bottom of the lower receiver and behind the magazine well), and gave it a quarter-turn to hold it in the 'out' position. While holding the magazine housing with the left hand, he grasped the pistol grip with the right hand, and, pressing the trigger all the way to the rear, rotated the pistol grip to the right; this turned the trigger and stock group free of the receiver, and the group could now be pulled to the rear and off the receiver. The bolt and telescoping operating-spring unit could be withdrawn by pulling the bolt handle back through the bolt-handle slot. Note that although the barrel of the MP 40 appeared to have been easily removed, it was actually locked into place by a stamped washer and was not meant to be removed. Reassembly was in reverse order.

The MP 38, MP 40 and MP 41 were issued with the M34 cleaning kit that was also standard issue with the Kar 98k bolt-action rifle. It consisted of a cleaning chain, cleaning brush, oil brush, oil dropper with cleaning oil, receiver-head wiper and cleaning wicks. The kit was held in a double-ended sheet-metal container.

LEFT
When disassembling an MP 40, it was important to ensure that the weapon was empty of any ammunition; the user would then remove the magazine and move the bolt forward. (AdeQ Historical Archives)

RIGHT
Here the receiver lock button is pulled. (AdeQ Historical Archives)

After holding the magazine housing and pressing the trigger, the receiver was then twisted, which in turn freed the stock group. (AdeQ Historical Archives)

During cleaning, the barrel had to be held in the left hand by the receiver, with the muzzle pointed downwards. The cleaning chain was used for pulling the brushes and cleaning wicks through the barrel. At one end of the chain was a link or eye. With this, the cleaning brush was hooked or a cleaning wick could be fitted. The cleaning chain was basically guided through from the barrel end to the chamber. The right hand guided the beginning of the chain from the chamber into the barrel and allowed it to slide through the barrel. With the chain hanging out of the muzzle the barrel was then inverted. With the left hand thereby securely holding the barrel, the right hand then gripped the chain hanging out and pulled the chain with the brush or wick several times through the barrel toward the muzzle.

The bristle brushes were referred to as the cleaning brush and oil brush. The cleaning brush cleaned out the residue found in the bore after shooting. This residue was diluted and loosened by applying cleaning oil to the front of the cleaning brush before pulling it through the bore. The oil brush served only for oiling the cleaned bore, and then the bore was wiped dry and cleaned of any remaining residues with the cleaning wicks. (The thin layer of remaining oil in the barrel helped prevent rust formation.) The cleaning and oil brush could only be oiled with the oil-dropper container, which featured a trickle valve. To pull the cleaning

LEFT
Once the receiver was free, the telescoping spring and bolt could be removed. (AdeQ Historical Archives)

RIGHT
Seen here are the telescoping spring and firing pin. The bolt was next to be removed, then cleaning of the weapon could begin. Reassembly was the same in reverse. Interestingly, the MP 40's telescoping spring and firing pin were nearly identical to those used in the earlier prototype MK 36.III developed by Hugo Schmeisser. (AdeQ Historical Archives)

German soldiers are seen here practising their skills in firing SMGs. According to the Luftwaffe manual *D (Luft) 5602/Die Ausbildung mit der Maschinenpistole 38 und 40*, in units equipped with the MP 38 and/or the MP 40, all officers as well as non-commissioned officers were to be trained. Responsibility for the training with and the maintenance of the weapon rested with the company's commanding officer. The correct guidance and supervision of the training was only possible if the company commander himself was familiar with the weapon and had mastered the training procedures. (AdeQ Historical Archives)

wicks through the barrel, these needed to be threaded through the middle of the eye of the cleaning chain.

A major cleaning of the MP 40 was done after each firing as well, as when the weapon became wet or dusty. This was a maintenance procedure as well as a preventative measure to avoid having the weapon succumb to rust. The major cleaning occurred in the following order:

First, the MP 40 was disassembled and the individual parts were laid onto a rag. Second, the user attached the cleaning brush to the cleaning chain, oiled it well and pulled it twice through the barrel from the chamber. After pulling through the cleaning brush and chain, he removed any abrasive dirt and oil with a patch. Third, he attached a dry cleaning wick on the chain and pulled it through from the chamber to the muzzle. If the wick was dirty after pulling through, it had to be replaced by a new, clean wick. The user replaced the wick and repeated the process until it came out clean. The bore was now clean. The oil brush had to be well oiled before being pulled through the chamber and bore once or twice with the cleaning chain. The blued-steel parts were then dabbed with a damp rag to wipe away dust and dirt. After this, the gun was dried, then all steel parts were lightly oiled with a cleaning wick dampened with weapon-cleaning oil.

The manuals for the MP 40 also recommended checking and cleaning the magazines. First, the user removed the follower and follower spring from the magazine housing. He then cleaned (with rags) and lightly greased the inner walls of the magazine housing, before inspecting the follower spring for strength (it sufficed when it was two windings longer than the magazine housing). Dented magazines or magazines to be stored were not to be filled with ammunition. It was recommended that, after filling the magazines, the first cartridge was pushed with the magazine filler another five or ten times downwards, until a lighter movement or rolling of the cartridges was felt.

OPERATIONAL HISTORY

Forerunners

It wasn't until the Chaco War (1932–35), between Bolivia and Paraguay, and the Spanish Civil War (1936–39), that the MP 28.II and other interwar SMGs received their first large-scale combat testing. The SMGs' performance during these conflicts in close-quarters combat, notably in urban environments, demonstrated the superiority of the handy, rapid-firing weapons over the bolt-action rifle; the rifle's long-range accuracy

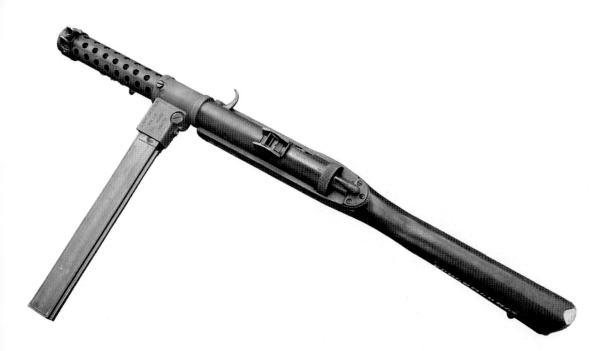

and greater reach were much less significant advantages in such settings. Round for round, the pistol ammunition used by SMGs was appreciably lighter than that used for rifles, so an individual soldier could carry more rounds. That said, it was already evident that ammunition supply was a very real issue for users of SMGs, and so considerable thought was given to how best to maximize ammunition carriage on the person, and the optimal way to resupply troops in combat conditions with ammunition. This problem would be addressed by using magazine pouches that could hold multiple magazines, issuing magazines (and drums) of various sizes to handle capacity, and employing bandoliers laden with ammunition for reloading the magazines.

These lessons were not lost on international observers, including those in Germany, the Soviet Union and the United States, although some – notably the British – continued to regard SMGs as 'gangster' weapons, capable of offering little advantage to well-trained, regular troops. To observers in Germany, however, the SMG appeared to offer a potent combination of firepower and portability to mobile troops such as motorized infantry and airborne soldiers. The SMG would become the quintessential section-leader's weapon across the German armed forces as war became ever more likely in the late 1930s.

The Lanchester, based upon the MP 28.II, was mainly used by Britain's Royal Navy. The Mk I*, seen here, could only be fired on full-automatic, unlike the original Mk I. Weapons like the Lanchester required substantial amounts of machining, and expensive components; note that the magazine housing is made of solid brass. The MP 38 and MP 40 would herald a new generation of inexpensively produced SMGs that would supplant these older weapons. (Leroy Thompson)

World War II

At the outset of its combat career, the MP 38 was intended to be used by armoured troops and specialized units such as the *Fallschirmjäger*. The addition of a resting bar underneath the barrel made it easier to fire the weapon from the ports of an armoured fighting vehicle while protecting the barrel from damage. The folding stock also made the MP 38 compact, and it could be fired either with the stock folded or with it extended.

The Finnish kp/31 Suomi became legendary in the hands of Finnish soldiers during the Winter War against the Soviet Union in 1939–40. This superbly engineered, reliable weapon was expensive to produce but was an export success, seeing service with the armed forces of several countries – not least Nazi Germany. (Leroy Thompson)

The outbreak of war in 1939 greatly increased Germany's demand for all weapons, including SMGs. Approximately 8,722 MP 38s were listed in the various inventory stocks of the Wehrmacht at the time of the invasion of Poland. 'The weapon performed well, but some problems did arise. The most serious deficiency noted was the lack of a reliable safety. Many casualties were inflicted on German troops by the inadvertent dropping or mishandling of the MP38' (Iannamico 1998: 62). The problem was remedied by various expedient means such as fabricating a leather strap to secure the bolt handle.

In April 1940, the MP 40 was adopted and the MP 38 was classified as limited standard. The MP 40 thus became the standard SMG of the Wehrmacht from 1940 to 1945. It was issued to the following personnel: company and platoon commanders, and to at least one member of each section, in all infantry units; to tank and vehicle crews; to parachute troops; and, as a special-purpose weapon. A typical World War II German infantry company was issued 16 SMGs, 78 rifles and 12 LMGs, ranking the MP 40 second only to the Mauser Kar 98k bolt-action rifle in total numbers in use by the German infantry. With increased production of the MP 40, virtually every seventh man in a division of approximately 10,000 men would be issued with SMGs after 1944; even more were scaled for airborne, armoured and motorized divisions.

In the standard German infantry squad, the squad leader (*Gruppenführer*) was armed with an SMG; his command role involved directing the fire and movement of his men, and he would use his personal weapon only at close quarters. The real source of firepower for the squad was the LMG and all the squad's activities, whether in attack or defence, centred on this weapon.

It is worth reflecting upon how the distribution of SMGs could have a significant effect on the firepower potential of a German infantry company. Taking the company structure outlined above, we see deeply contrasting rates of the fire. As already indicated, at the top of the firepower tree were the machine guns, which in the German Army's case meant the MG 34 or MG 42, both firing the 7.92×57mm Mauser cartridge. The older MG 34, a high-quality machined weapon, had a rate of fire of 800–900rds/min, while the MG 42 could deliver fire up to 1,200rds/min. These are cyclical rates, however; practical rates of fire would be more in the region of 200–250rds/min. Any faster than this, and the machine gunners ran the serious risk of either running out of ammunition, burning through their barrels or producing 'cook-offs' (premature ignition of ammunition, caused by excessive heat build-up in the chamber).

At the opposite pole to the machine gun was the Mauser Kar 98k rifle. A well-trained rifleman was capable of firing around 15rds/min, dependent upon rapid operation of the bolt and allowing for two reloadings of the five-round box magazine. Therefore, the seven rifle-armed men of a ten-man infantry squad (up to October 1943) were theoretically capable of 105rds/min, although the realities of combat would typically ensure less than this figure. Therefore, a single machine gun in each squad could produce more firepower than seven riflemen. Yet at close ranges, so too could the squad leader, with his MP 40. Total magazine-loaded ammunition carried by this individual was up to 224 rounds (six magazines stored in pouches and one loaded into the gun), and each magazine could,

This group of German troops in Yugoslavia includes one man armed with an MP 41. (Cody Images)

Members of the Deutsches Afrikakorps armed with MP 38s are seen marching to embark on their transports to fight in Libya. Note the various manners in which the SMGs were carried. (AdeQ Historical Archives)

if necessary, be drained through the gun in around four seconds, during which time the riflemen might have only managed one shot each. (The low-powered 9mm round meant that SMGs rarely experienced the heat build-up and cook-off problems encountered by medium and heavy machine guns, although relentless rapid fire could indeed lead to some malfunctions.) Again, practical operation of the weapon meant that a soldier was unlikely to burn through a magazine in one hit, but such fire could prove useful, especially if delivering mobile short-range suppression to allow the rest of the squad to close up.

What is especially revealing is the changing nature of MP 40 distribution amongst the squad as the war went on. The German invasion of the Soviet Union in 1941 forced the Germans to confront the threat of an army heavily armed with SMGs, particularly once distribution of the PPSh-41 and PPS-43 became very widespread from 1942 and 1943. German forces were stunned at the massive volumes of firepower the Soviets could generate during infantry engagements, not least because the ubiquitous PPSh-41 had a 900rds/min rate of fire. This experience informed a significant change in German divisional organization in October 1943, which had an impact on the squad composition. The ten-man squad was reduced to nine men, but the weapons carried by the squad were six rifles, two SMGs, a machine gun and a pistol. Here we note that despite the drop of one man from the squad, the firepower of the unit has significantly increased with the addition of another SMG. The change also reflects the fact that many of the engagements the Germans were fighting were at close ranges, fought in the cities of Ukraine and Russia, or the mountainous terrain of Italy and the Balkans.

In late 1944 and 1945, the movement towards automatic weapons at the squad level intensified further. One advantage of SMGs is that they take less time to train someone in their effective use when compared to a bolt-action rifle. (A precision rifle shot takes sophisticated control of breathing and body mechanics, whereas an SMG requires less sophisticated handling.) Germany was starting to scrape the bottom of the manpower barrel by this time, so any weapon that could reduce training times was welcomed. Furthermore, the battles were pushing through the major cities of Western and Eastern Europe, and the SMG was king in the close-range urban duel. The urgencies of the late-war period produced a further change in squad organization, as historian Stephen Bull here describes:

The Volksgrenadier divisions of late 1944 were effectively ordinary infantry divisions following rebuilding and re-organization. In these, although there were still nine men to a squad, these were either 'rifle' or sub-machine gun squads. In the rifle squads the armament stayed the same as previously, while SMG squads were supposed to be armed entirely with that weapon. The exception to the rule was to be the one squad within each 'SMG' platoon which carried three rifles and five SMGs in addition to the LMG and pistol; presumably the idea was to give the SMG units some longer-range firepower, but shortage of automatic weapons may also have played a part. (Bull 2004: 24)

The shift towards SMG firepower here described by Bull reflects substantially the Soviet practice of arming entire units purely with SMGs. The thinking behind this policy was solid. Nine men armed with MP 40s would have been able to put literally hundreds of rounds on target in a short space of time, delivering attrition and suppression in a rippling barrage of fire. The preponderance of SMGs would also give the Germans more of a fighting chance against the SMG-armed Soviets in the east, and the Americans in the west, who were armed with the semi-automatic M1 Garand rifle, the .45 M1A1 Thompson SMG and the M1 Carbine.

Bull's analysis goes on to mention the introduction of the MP 44/StG 44 assault rifle later in the war, and the fact that the German forces aspired to replace the MP 40 with such weapons. The StG 44 was certainly a new generation of firearm, its 7.92×33mm cartridge performing well over ranges up to 600m, but with low enough recoil for the user to deliver full-auto fire comfortably. The StG 44 was a glimpse of the future of firearms (see 'Impact' section below), but its production limitations meant that the MP 40 would stay as the major full-auto close-range firearm of the German Army until the end of the war.

This member of the French Resistance correctly holds her captured MP 40 in the firing position during the liberation of Paris in 1944. (AdeQ Historical Archives)

Fighting performance

The first significant use of the MP 38 and MP 40 was during the invasion of France and the Low Countries. The extended vertical magazine located beneath the MP 38 and MP 40 soon proved to be problematic when firing from the prone or lying position, as it forced the shooter to expose more of his upper body. The vertical magazine position of the MP 40 also meant the shooter needed to be familiar with the weapon's specific requirements. Despite the existence of numerous period photographs showing German (and Allied) soldiers firing the MP 40 by holding the magazine, the manual specified that the magazine well should be grasped while firing. Following the proper procedure reduced the possibility of misfires and other problems associated with stick magazines.

A warning was issued on 4 June 1940 regarding accidental discharges experienced when inserting a magazine into the MP 38. The eventual fix to the problem was to redesign the bolt handle assembly; a new notch was cut on the receiver's

45

bolt handle slot, and the notch enabled the bolt handle to be locked in the forward or closed position. While keeping the bolt in the forward position was done as a means of safety, it also kept dirt and other debris from entering the weapon's receiver through the ejection port or bolt-handle slot.

Although late in the war the Germans would manufacture copies of the British Sten, which had a side-mounted magazine, they went on to design the MP 3008 (see below) with a bottom-mounted magazine. (Even fine post-war weapons such as the Heckler & Koch MP5 SMG retained the bottom-mounted magazine.) However, the compact nature of the MP 38 and MP 40, when the stock was folded, enabled these weapons to be fired from a variety of positions that a fixed-stock SMG of the period wouldn't permit. In addition, the weapon could be easily concealed and still be readily employed, as shown by this account of its use by the 'Brandenburgers' (German Army special forces) during the invasion of the Netherlands:

> On the morning of 10 May 1940 two of the [Brandenburgers], disguised as Dutch military police, escorted six German 'prisoners' to the bridge. The compact size of the MP38 meant it could be strapped to the chests of each of the 'prisoners', hidden under a greatcoat. Within moments they had overpowered the guards on the German side of the bridge and severed the detonation wires for the demolition explosives. Once they had informed the guards on the Dutch side that they were crossing with prisoners, the telephone connections were cut. At the other side, the Dutch escorted the 'prisoners' away in a truck. The still-disguised Germans who remained behind captured the surviving guardhouse with support from the rest of their unit. A German armoured train, closely followed by a troop train, then crossed the bridge. Meanwhile the 'prisoners' escaped their captors and attacked several Dutch strongpoints along the river, taking 40 prisoners themselves. (Ingram 2001: 60)

Operators of the MP 38 and MP 40 were forced to adapt to firing in short bursts, so as to avoid muzzle climb and conserve ammunition. In time, the

Crete 1941 (previous pages)

On 20 May 1941, Germany invaded the Greek island of Crete in *Unternehmen Merkur* (Operation *Mercury*), using *Fallschirmjäger* (airborne troops) in large numbers. The next day the Germans captured Maleme airfield, allowing them to ferry in reinforcements by air; after only ten or so days of fighting, the island had fallen to the Axis, but the extremely high casualties suffered by the German airborne forces demonstrated to the German high command that a repeat of such an operation would not be feasible, and plans to invade.

The two *Fallschirmjäger* depicted here sitting behind a stone wall have been cleaning and loading their weapons when a suspicious sound has alerted them. One soldier has taken the upper section off from the lower receiver of his MP 38; he has twisted off the upper-barrel receiver tube from the lower receiver and is pulling out the bolt assembly. The other man is armed with an MP 40; 9mm rounds are piled up atop his folded camouflage *Zeltbahn* (shelter-quarter) in front of him.

Germans and their enemies were able to recognize the distinctive sounds that their SMGs made. From these sounds, a soldier could work out whether fire was that of friend or foe, as well as pinpointing the position from which the weapon was firing. For example, Lieutenant Carl Howard Cartledge of the 1st Regimental Recon, 501st Parachute Infantry Regiment, 101st Airborne Division, told how the MP 40s that his unit had captured were modified to change their audible report. The paratroopers had occupied an enemy position near a dike at Heteren in the Netherlands. They had captured a number of MG 34s and MP 40s, as well as substantial quantities of ammunition, from the Germans:

Fallschirmjäger raiding Tito's headquarters in Yugoslavia in June 1944. Of interest is the variety of weapons depicted in this image: MP 40, MG 42, Kar 98k, and a P 08 Luger pistol. (AdeQ Historical Archives)

> By this time in the Holland invasion, the Germans used the MP40 in a defensive manner. If an MP40 gunner cranked at night, the [American] mortar man knew he was in a patrol. They spread the clicks slightly and dropped four down the tubes simultaneously. The four rounds fell out of the sky within a split second of each other, virtually eliminating any time to duck … A Nazi scream would acknowledge the results … If we were going to shoot German guns we knew we needed an edge. (Quoted in Iannamico 1998: 149)

To prevent being fired upon by their own side, the American paratroopers devised an ingenious plan:

> We took out some wire cutters and began experimenting... We cut about two inches [5cm] from the recoil springs of the MG34s and the

MP40s. We made no other modifications. The shortened recoil springs changed the cyclic rate and the sounds of the guns. The different sounds told the mortar crews that the 'Screaming Eagles' held the brick factory. (Quoted in Iannamico 1998: 149)

Lieutenant Cartledge found the MP 40 'to be a good weapon with a flimsy stock. The stock didn't matter as an experienced sub gunner doesn't use it' (quoted in Iannamico 1998: 149). That night the captured MP 40s and ammunition were well used in the fight against the Germans during that battle.

Regardless of the combat conditions, every soldier issued with the MP 38 or MP 40 constantly had to make sure that his weapon was in good working order and that it was regularly cleaned and properly maintained. Even so, the invasion of the Soviet Union in June 1941 and the prolonged winter fighting that ensued provided a major additional challenge for all kinds of weapon systems employed by the Germans. While fighting in winter conditions, standard infantry and *Gebirgsjäger* (mountain troops) alike found that when using the MP 40, the major concern was to prevent snow and ice from entering the receiver (either from snowfall or freezing rain or from dropping the gun in the snow) and freezing up the recoil springs. A special canvas cover was made to be used with the MP 40 in order to prevent debris from entering the receiver.

There are numerous Soviet accounts detailing the use of the SMG by the Germans during World War II. The legendary Russian sniper, Vassili Zaitsev, notes how he was wounded in one encounter:

I made ready to dash after him, but the enemy spotted us and opened up with rifles and submachine guns. Something scorched my right leg, and immediately the leg felt much heavier. It was difficult to drag it

The MP 38 bolt could be held back in a safe manner by using a notch located above the slot, as depicted in this wartime illustration. The bolt charging handle shown here is an early version, later replaced with one that was modified to be pushed in as an added safety feature. (AdeQ Historical Archives)

across the floor. I inched slowly over to Misha, while the enemy kept on shooting. By the time I reached Misha, my trousers were drenched in blood. (Zaitsev 2009: 53)

From 1943, German *Jäger* companies, organized akin to their comrades in the standard infantry companies, eschewed the bolt-action rifle altogether and were – except for the LMG section – equipped entirely with SMGs (Ingram 2001: 65). On the Western Front, a Canadian battle report was made in 1944 covering the MP 40's role in small-group actions:

> Experience has shown that the Germans will almost invariably launch a counter-attack to break up an attack by small infantry units. You can expect such a counter-attack, usually by 10 to 20 men, not more than five minutes after you get close to the German positions. They are usually well armed with light machine guns and machine pistols, and counter attack by fire and movement. They keep up heavy fire while small details, even individuals, alternately push forward. The Germans almost always attack your flank. They seldom close with bayonet, but try to drive you out by fire. (Quoted in Ingram 2001: 73)

The effectiveness and advanced design of the MP 40 were so obvious that all the important nations began to adopt SMGs for their own military forces. Many countries involved in World War II developed SMGs with similar features to those of the MP 40 – notably the folding stock, the use of the magazine as a front handgrip, and the production techniques employed.

Comparative performance

It is now clear that the MP 38 and MP 40 transformed the potential of the German infantry on the battlefield. The portability and full-auto fire of the weapons made them ideally suited to short-range suppression and close-quarters killing, and just two or three of the SMGs could make life dangerous for an entire platoon of enemy soldiers. But how did the MP 40 compare to similar enemy weapons, and what does this comparison tell us about the German SMG?

One of the sincerest forms of flattery for any weapon is when it is adopted by enemy forces in preference to their own firearms. The flattery is not to be taken too far – soldiers are often naturally attracted to collecting the enemy's kit and equipment, if only for the novelty or resale value. Furthermore, being on the receiving end of enemy fire frequently results in myths and exaggerations about opposing technology. Also, we have to remember that on the Eastern Front severe shortages of weapons amongst the Soviets, particularly in 1941–42, plus the desire for infantrymen to ditch their rifles in favour of full-auto weapons, made collection of German SMGs desirable.

Certainly, the Red Army and its partisan allies made good use of captured MP 40s against their former owners. In many cases, these SMGs were prized souvenirs that were highly valued by their Allied liberators. Here Zaitsev recounts another event during the battle for Stalingrad:

When we reached the entrance to the bunker, a German lance corporal with a submachine gun around his neck was sheltering from the rain underneath a lady's parasol. Afinogenov crawled into the trench. His knife glistened in the darkness. He stabbed the sentry in the heart and muffled the Nazi's groans with his hand. The lance corporal collapsed without a sound. Scherbina and Afinogenov remained as lookouts on top while Kryakhov and I silently slipped into the trenches below. I quickly took in my surroundings. By the door there was a rack of nails pounded into the wall. From each nail hung a submachine gun. Beneath the guns were helmets, and by the helmets, torches. Everything was very orderly, in typical German style. All up and down the sides of the bunker were cots, with German soldiers snoring peacefully beneath their blankets. Their uniforms hung above their heads. In the centre of the room was a small electric lamp, which bathed the bunker in a dim milky light. Kryakhov and I took a couple of submachine guns from the rack for souvenirs. Kryakhov unscrewed the light bulb from the overhead lamp, and we each clipped a torch to our belt. Meanwhile the Germans kept snoring. Stepan Kryakhov gave a loud and firm command: 'For the murders of our mothers and children at the hands of these fascist swine – fire!' Our submachine guns spat out streams of hot lead. The Nazis were rudely jerked awake. They looked like marionettes being yanked on broken strings. They collapsed in their bunks, moaning and screaming until the arcs of flying lead raked over them again and shut them up. Their blankets were thrown in heaps of confusion. (Zaitsev 2009: 114)

There are several photographs of Russian soldiers armed with MP 40s, but there are far more of German soldiers utilizing PPSh-41s. The reasons for this are not difficult to see. A PPSh-41 had a far higher rate of fire than the MP 40 (900rds/min as opposed to 500rds/min). Although a higher rate of fire is not necessarily the acid test of SMG superiority, the German troops on the Eastern Front would have sobering experiences of the raking fire of the Soviet guns, particularly as by the end of the war the Soviets had a higher percentage of their front-line soldiers armed with SMGs. PPSh-41s, in their unloaded state, were nearly 0.25kg lighter than an MP 40, despite the latter's skeleton stock.

There were also reliability issues. As noted above, the Eastern Front was an unforgiving place for small arms, with dirt, dust, snow and ice constantly invading gun mechanisms and grinding them to a halt. The MP 40 was particularly vulnerable

Bulgarian partisans armed with the following SMGs, from left to right: Soviet PPSh-41, MP 41 and MP 40. A very rare wartime image of the MP 41 in use by forces opposing the Germans, along with the MP 40. (AdeQ Historical Archives)

to damage to its single-stack 32-round magazine, and to dirt intrusion through the large ejection port on the upper receiver, even with the issue of the receiver cover. The PPSh-41, by contrast, was a model of Soviet reliability, having enough 'play' in the mechanism to tolerate all manner of rough handling and insanitary conditions. An illuminating account of the contrast between the MP 40 and the PPSh-41 comes from Russian tank rider Lieutenant Yevgeni Bessonov in 1945:

> At dawn on 22 April we approached a high railway embankment and were stopped by intensive fire. We could quickly have destroyed the German delaying force and moved on forward, but the problem was that the passage under the railway bridge was filled with sand and fortified with big logs, connected with metal girders. We did not manage to destroy that barricade... We rode on tanks for some time and all of a sudden came under fire from trenches on the right-hand side of the road. The tanks stopped, I ordered, 'Dismount! Fire!' and the whole company ran towards those trenches firing non-stop from our submachine guns. Right in front of me was a Fritz in a trench. I tried to cut him down with my German submachine gun, but apparently during the skirmish at the embankment some sand had got into the bolt. I jerked the bolt, pulled the trigger, but it did not fire. The German did not think long, grabbed his rifle and aimed it at me ... Right at that time a submachine gun burst sounded in the air and the German dropped dead at the bottom of the trench. It turned out that it was Drozd who cut him down with a Soviet PPsh submachine gun, which never jammed in battle. Why the hell did I carry that German submachine gun? We jumped across the trenches, some Germans fled, while the rest were killed. Andrey took away my submachine gun, took out the magazine and threw the submachine gun away. (Bull 2011: 243–44)

The account here presents a stark contrast between the robust PPSh-41 and the more vulnerable MP 40. Arguably on the Eastern Front, the Soviet weapon had the edge in terms of being a practical combat weapon. In addition, the PPSh-41 had a selector switch, meaning that the operator could opt for more accurate or frugal single-shot fire, should the situation warrant it.

Yet the comparison is not entirely one-sided. Although the MP 40 was not quite as reliable as the PPSh-41, with decent battlefield cleaning and handling it would generally operate without serious or repeated malfunctions, as US tests later confirmed (see below). The PPSh-41 could rip through a magazine more quickly, but it also had greater problems with muzzle climb. This tendency was partly, not entirely, corrected by its muzzle brake, but in turn this feature produced a dazzling muzzle flash in low-light or night-time conditions and a hefty report. The MP 40, by contrast, had a perfectly manageable muzzle climb and was more accurate when accuracy was needed. Also, although the 7.62×25mm in the PPSh-41 had better penetration than the MP 40's 9mm round, this didn't necessarily equate to manstopping power. The 9mm arrested better inside the victim's body, delivering more of its kinetic punch to the target.

The Americans also took a keen interest in the German small arms, and conducted several comparative tests, providing invaluable material for later firearms historians. For example, personnel from the US Army Ordnance Research Center conducted a series of tests on a captured MP 40 between 30 December 1942 and 14 January 1943 at Aberdeen Proving Grounds, Maryland. They found that:

> The Schmeisser placed eighty-one out of one hundred shots on the standard 6'×6' target at fifty yards when fired full-automatic from the off hand position. The M3 in either caliber, consistently averages from 92 to 98 hits in this type of fire. The testers of the German weapon noted, however, that the lock on the folding stock of the test gun was so worn as to permit considerable play between the stock and the gun. It was felt that the Schmeisser was actually more accurate than was indicated by the test. (US Army 1943)

While firing the weapon off hand, the testers obtained 78 hits 'in firing 100 shots at the 6'×6' target at a range of 100 yards. The firers reported that the comparatively high cyclic rate (518 rounds per minute) of the weapon and the absence of a fire selector made single-shot firing almost impossible' (US Army 1943). The Americans further subjected the weapon to various conditions to study how it performed. The endurance test resulted in 5,500 rounds being fired without any breakages and only five minor malfunctions noted (failure to feed, failure to eject, light firing-pin blows, etc.). Other tests included subjecting the weapon to dust, mud, rain and sand. The researchers summarized their findings with the following statement in their report:

> It was concluded that the general functioning of the Schmeisser was excellent and that its accuracy was very good. Disassambly and assembly were considerably more complicated than with the M3 and could not be accomplished without tools. On a basis of 100 the

Warsaw 1944 (previous pages)

On 1 August 1944 the Armia Krajowa (Home Army), a Polish resistance organization, launched their bid to liberate Warsaw from Nazi Germany. Although the uprising was intended to coincide with the arrival of Stalin's forces around the Polish capital, the Soviet advance was deliberately halted by the Soviet leader, allowing the Germans to crush the uprising and destroy the city in nine weeks of savage fighting.

The three German combatants shown here are moving between areas of cover, exposing them to sniper fire that has just hit the rearmost man. They are approaching the body of a member of the Armia Krajowa armed with a Błyskawica SMG, a weapon modelled on the MP 40. The SS man on the left, a member of 5. SS-Panzer-Division *Wiking*, wears full kit with a pair of MP 38/40 magazine pouches and is armed with an MP 38. The SS man in the centre is a member of the 'Dirlewanger' Brigade and is armed with an MP 40. On the right is a member of the SD armed with an MP 41 with its distinctive wooden stock.

Schmeisser was given a rating of 79 as compared with the 95 rating accorded the U.S. Submachine Gun, cal .45 M3. – END OF REPORT. (US Army 1943)

In an unrelated evaluation of the German MP 40 (Technical Intelligence, HRPE Report No. 63, dated 11 August 1944), the reporting officer compared the penetration power between the 9mm MP 40 and the .45 ACP Thompson M1A1 SMG. He wrote: 'at a range of 25 yds. we fired at an American helmet with a German machine-pistol and our Tommy Gun. The German pistol penetrated the helmet and started to come out the other side whereas our Tommy Gun made a big dent, but no penetration' (quoted in Iannamico 1998: 92). This comparison confirms the penetrative capability of the MP 40, even when compared to a big, heavy round like the .45 ACP. The 9mm Parabellum retained its penetrative force better over 200m, and this could make a critical difference when shooting through doors, wooden partitions and all the other obstacles that were common during urban encounters. In woodland engagements, the better penetration of the 9mm also meant that the bullet would be less likely to deviate when passing through light features such as leaves and small twigs.

Overall, the Americans were impressed by the fact that the MP 40 was rugged, inexpensive and could be made easily from non-critical materials. The negatives included the complicated manner of disassembly and the lack of interchangeability of certain parts when compared with other captured MP 40s. These lessons would prompt the US Army to develop future SMGs with parts that were completely interchangeable.

During the war, the MP 38 and MP 40 were prized weapons that were captured by the Resistance and partisan units and used against their former owners. Seen here is one of Marshal Tito's partisans armed with an MP 40 in war-torn Yugoslavia. (AdeQ Historical Archives)

Comparisons between the MP 40 and the Thompson M1/M1A1 are as illuminating as those between the German gun and the PPSh-41. The greatest distinction was in terms of weight. Many GIs took up the MP 40 simply because it weighed 3.97kg, compared to the arm-deadening burden of the M1, at 4.82kg. Such a weight difference would make a huge difference to a soldier on the battlefield, both in lugging his weapon over long distances and moving it quickly onto target during combat. The Thompson had an extremely powerful round – the .45 ACP – but as the test data above shows, the manstopping capabilities of the .45 ACP didn't give it the penetration of the 9mm. This being said, the Thompson fired at a cyclical rate of 700rds/min, 200rds/min faster than the MP 40. The American gun also found favour with some German soldiers. Here a British soldier recounts what he found during street fighting in the Netherlands late in the war:

When we got into Holland we were involved in a lot of house to house fighting. Street fighting could be hard as there could be a Jerry in the next house, or even the next room. Once we kicked in a front door and heard them leaving by the back. We killed some after a fight across a street in Den Hag when our Bren was able to outshoot them. When we searched the house, there were three dead Jerries all with captured Thompsons and American web belts for the magazines. They seemed to like them too but they were no good at long-range fighting. (Pegler 2010: 70)

This pair of British soldiers, pictured in 1944, includes a lance corporal armed with an MP 40. Since the British also utilized the 9mm round it proved feasible for British and Commonwealth troops to use captured MP 38s and MP 40s. Note the non-regulation form of firing by grasping the magazine. (Cody Images)

The fact that all the Germans here were armed with Thompsons is worth comment, especially as the Thompson's .45 ACP ammunition meant that the guns weren't compatible with the German forces' own ammunition stocks. To keep their Thompsons working, therefore, the Germans would have had to replenish their ammunition from captured supplies. If they used the British Sten (unlikely, given the comments I will make below), by contrast, the German troops could utilize their own universal 9mm Parabellum ammunition. The Germans would certainly appreciate the Thompson's rugged reliability, as they would its terminal effects on human opponents at close ranges. It may well have been that the unit captured a supply of Thompsons and ammunition in one lot, thereby making arming the unit homogenously a sensible decision. Or it could simply be the case that previously the men had been armed with Kar 98k rifles. In the street battles of the Netherlands, these would not be the best weapons for the job, and if MP 40s weren't available then simply swapping to captured Thompsons would be a practical option.

One other point to note about this quotation is the statement that 'our Bren was able to outshoot them'. Even had the soldiers been armed with MP 40s, the chances are that the Germans would still have met their end under the Bren fire. Even given the rapid-fire capabilities of the MP 40, soldiers armed with these weapons still had to pick their battles carefully. If engaged by machine guns at ranges beyond 150m, SMG-armed soldiers were at a critical disadvantage, and would have to rely on their own side's MGs and rifles to provide long-range suppression. Only if they could close the distance under cover could they hope to redress the balance. (At ranges of under 50m, the operators moving in from the flanks, the advantage would likely be on the side of the SMGs.) The SMG-armed soldier always had to fight within a certain set of advantages and compromises, utilizing short-range firepower to its maximum, but recognizing the critical limitations when it came to range.

The production war

Above we mentioned the Sten machine gun, effectively the British equivalent to the MP 40. The Sten ranks as one of the crudest SMGs of World War II, certainly inferior to the MP 40. Both guns had a similar rate of fire, and near-identical ballistic performance on account of their shared ammunition type. The Sten, however, was an unpredictable weapon, prone to jamming and misfiring. This quality made it a poor trade for the MP 40, hence in photographs we see few German soldiers using the weapon.

Yet the Sten had one advantage over the MP 40. It was present in far larger numbers. Here is where the MP 40 falls down in many regards against the Allied SMGs. Production totals for the MP 40 were as follows:

1940	1941	1942	1943	1944
113,700	239,300	231,500	234,500	228,600

The total output for these years is 1,047,600 units. In themselves these are impressive figures, but what is significant here is how the production figures peaked so early in the war (1941), but then effectively declined thereafter. In other aspects of armament production in the Third Reich – such as tanks, aircraft and submarines – production capacity increased, peaking dramatically in 1944.

The reasons for the MP 40 production figures are bound up with several factors. One is the increasing output of other small arms in the later years of the war. One of the great problems of German war manufacturing was its over-diversification of products, from which the world of small arms was not immune. During the later years of the war, the German armament industry not only had to churn out hundreds of thousands of standard rifles, machine guns and SMGs, but it also produced 400,000 Gew 43 semi-auto rifles. The StG 44 figures are even more revealing. In 1943, 19,501 StG 44s were produced, then leaping to 281,860 in 1944 and 124,616 in 1945. In the critical year of the war, 1944, just before the Reich began its complete collapse, the German small-arms industry was evidently focusing on assault-rifle production, not MP 40s.

Turning back to the Sten, against nearly 1.5 million MP 40s produced, some four million Stens were made between 1941 and 1945. The Soviets churned out some six million PPSh-41s and the United States produced 1.5 million Thompsons and 700,000 M3s (the latter despite the gun only being designed in 1942). The simple fact was that the distribution of the MP 40 was not sufficient to keep up with the volume of SMGs delivered by the Allied industrial monster. The MP 40 could hold up individually against any of the SMGs possessed by the Allies, but ultimately it could compete in terms of numbers.

IMPACT
An influential SMG

The MP 40's impact was undoubtedly greatest during World War II, if only for the fact of the thousands of lives it took on the battlefield. We can only speculate, but had MP 40s not been available for battles such as those in Stalingrad, Kharkov, Caen, Arnhem and Berlin, then the Allied casualties might conceivably have been fewer. Yet the effective design of the MP 40 ensured that it had a wider impact on military history of the 20th century. We can define this impact in three main areas: (1) the production of wartime copies and derivatives; (2) the production of the same in the post-war era; and (3) the use of the MP 38 or MP 40 in post-war conflicts.

WARTIME COPIES AND DERIVATIVES

Even during World War II, many of Germany's opponents were influenced by the MP 40's distinctive design. By the war's end the Germans themselves, combining Allied SMG ideas with their own, would produce a 'last-ditch' SMG that owed its origins to the MP 40.

The Błyskawica ('Lightning') SMG was designed by Polish engineers Wacław Zawrotny and Seweryn Wielanier for the Polish Resistance, the Armia Krajowa ('Home Army'), in 1942–43. It was conceived and developed in such a way that it could be built in small, improvised workshops using screws rather than more up-to-date technologies. The weapon's folding buttstock and the location of the 32-round bottom-mounted magazine were inspired by the MP 40 while the internal mechanism owed much to the British Sten, also covertly manufactured in various areas of Occupied Europe. However, the Błyskawica had a free-floating firing pin rather than the fixed firing pin of the British weapon.

The Polish Armia Krajowa built a clandestine arms factory where it developed the Błyskawica SMG. The weapon was inspired by the German MP 40 and the British Sten. Designed in 1943 and produced in 1944, the Błyskawica saw service in the Warsaw Uprising (1 August–2 October 1944). (AdeQ Historical Archives)

Offering full-automatic fire only, it fired the 9mm cartridge employed by the Germans, as the designers wished to allow Polish combatants to use captured MP 40 ammunition. A prototype was built by September 1943 and, following approval by August Emil Fieldorf, the head of the Kierownictwo Dywersji (KeDyw; Directorate for Subversion), 1,300 were ordered and roughly 640 actually produced. After World War II a copy of the Błyskawica was made by the Argentine firm Hispano Argentina Fábrica de Automóviles Sociedad Anónima (HAFDASA).

The evident success of the MP 40 urged the Western Allies to begin work on their own versions of similar inexpensive sheet-metal weapon designs. The British Sten has already been mentioned, but the Americans also looked to the MP 40 for inspiration. While designing the .45-calibre M3 SMG in 1941–43, US engineers considered some features of the Sten and captured examples of the MP 40. The resultant weapon had a telescoping wire stock and bottom-mounted 30-round box magazine based on the Sten magazine; it arrived on the front lines too late to replace the Thompson as had been intended, but the improved M3A1 variant remained in service with US and other forces into the 1990s.

The Soviets also drew some inspiration from the MP 38 and MP 40 in their wartime small-arms production. Chambered in 7.62×25mm Tokarev and employing a curved 35-round box magazine, Alexei Sudayev's PPS-42 and PPS-43 SMGs were intended to be compact personal defence weapons. They were developed to fulfil the need for a cheaper, easier-to-produce equivalent to the PPSh-41, the Soviets' primary front-line SMG. As well as adopting sheet-metal construction for the PPS weapons, the Soviets produced a near-exact copy of the MP 40's folding stock for their PPS-43. The difference between the MP 40 and PPS-43 was that the latter's stock folded up and over the receiver top cover; the Soviet weapon could still be fired with the stock folded.

This member of the Prague police is armed with the MP 3008 in post-war Czechoslovakia. While the late-war German MP 3008 was based on the wartime British Sten, it utilized a common component of the MP 40 – its magazine. Some 10,000 were produced in the last months of World War II. (AdeQ Historical Archives)

POST-WAR COPIES AND VARIANTS

After World War II, the MP 40 continued to influence the creation of other SMGs, either cosmetically, internally or both. For example, the Kalashnikov series of assault rifles (AK, AKM, etc.) copied the folding stock of the MP 40. Many other weapons were also inspired by the German design.

Adopted by the Portuguese military in 1948, the 9×19mm FBP m/948 was the brainchild of Gonçalves Cardoso. It drew heavily upon the MP 40, copying its large bolt and telescoping operating spring but employing a fixed firing pin that was integral with the bolt block. Consequently the telescoping recoil system was 'flat nosed', without the attachment of the firing pin. The bolt was fitted with the standard MP 40 'push/pull' safety system and a 9mm Sten magazine-catch system. The FBP had a wire telescoping shoulder stock and MP 40-style magazine; it could be fitted with a rifle bayonet. The later m/963 and m/976 models offered select-fire capability.

Pictured in Angola in 1963, this Portuguese soldier is armed with an FBP m/948. This example lacks the optional bayonet lug and has its stock partially retracted. (Cody Images)

The Uzi's lethal combination of compactness, reliability and devastating firepower has ensured its lasting success across the world in the hands of military and law-enforcement personnel. The wooden stock fitted to this early example could hold cleaning oil and a bottle of gun oil behind the butt plate. (Cody Images)

Developed by Israel's Major Uziel Gal in the years after World War II, the Uzi entered service in 1954 and would be a standard-issue front-line weapon for decades. The Uzi drew several of its most distinctive features, such as the location of the magazine in the pistol grip, from a slew of innovative Czech designs of the immediate post-war period that originated in Jaroslav Holeček's ZK 476. However, Major Gal copied some of the features of the MP 40 in his design of the Uzi. For example, the collar nut that locks the barrel to the receiver is an almost exact copy of the system used by the MP 38 and MP 40. Uziel had ready access to the MP 38 and MP 40 since the Israel Defense Forces used large numbers of these German weapons immediately after World War II.

The 7.62×25mm M56, a Yugoslavian SMG, is a direct copy of the MP 40, but has a curved 32-round magazine owing to the shape of its

Yugoslav women soldiers carry their M56 SMGs as they undergo training, 1971. The M56 was designed with a lug to carry a bayonet. (AdeQ Historical Archives)

7.62×25mm ammunition. The M56 offers a range superior to that of its German counterpart; its 7.62×25mm cartridge provides significantly more penetration than the 9×19mm round used by the MP 40, although the Tokarev round lacks the stopping power of the German round (worldguns.ru).

The Spanish Star Z-45 was manufactured by Star Bonifacio Echeverría Sociedad Anónima. It draws heavily upon the MP 40 for its internal design, but utilizes wood for the pistol grip and forend. The Star Z-45 offers select-fire capability, with selection being made through the pull of the trigger; a short pull produces single shots, while a long pull produces full-automatic fire (worldguns.ru). The Star Z-45 was produced in a variety of calibres, including 9mm Largo, 9mm Parabellum, .38 Super and .45 ACP, and saw lengthy and successful service with military and law-enforcement personnel in Spain and parts of Latin America.

Yugoslavia 1990s (opposite)

After the death of Yugoslavia's Marshal Tito in 1980, that state's various ethnic regions began breaking apart. The former Yugoslavia was plunged into conflict for almost a decade as Bosnians, Serbians, Macedonians, Slovenians and Albanians fought to establish their own independent states. This scene shows three Bosnian soldiers of the Army of the Republic of Bosnia and Herzegovina taking cover and firing from makeshift defensive positions. At the top, one man is firing his AK with an MP 40-style shoulder stock folded forward. The next soldier (centre) is preparing to fire his M56 SMG, which has a bayonet affixed. Though chambered in a different calibre, the weapon is a direct copy of the MP 40. The crouching third man has an MP 40 slung on his back without a magazine, and holds an MG 42. Examples of this weapon captured in Yugoslavia at the end of World War II entered service with the Yugoslav Army as the M53/42, while Yugoslavia licence-built the MG 42 at the state-owned Zavodi Crvena Zastava company as the M53, retaining the 7.92×57mm Mauser calibre.

During Israel's fight for survival from 1948 to 1966, numerous leftover World War II German small arms were sent over to Israel by Eastern Bloc countries such as Czechoslovakia and Yugoslavia. As well as Kar 98k rifles and MG 34 and MG 42 machine guns, there were MP 40s. Seen here are Israeli special forces armed with MP 40s during a night-time operation, c. 1960. (AdeQ Historical Archives)

POST-WAR USE OF THE MP 40

After the surrender of the Wehrmacht in 1945, massive amounts of German firearms were left behind in the once-occupied countries. Some nations chose to arm sections of their own armies with the MP 40. Czechoslovakia, Norway, Austria, France, Yugoslavia and Bulgaria were countries that adopted the MP 38 and MP 40 in this way. Even Israel acquired a large stockpile of MP 40s from Czechoslovakia and used them effectively during the 1948 War of Independence and subsequent conflicts. Quantities of MP 40s were used by both sides during the Greek Civil War from 1946 to 1949. The Soviets aided emerging communist states behind the Iron Curtain with small arms captured from the Germans. They even clandestinely distributed their stockpile of captured MP 40s to communist movements around the world, especially in Asia as well as in Central and South America.

The French Army captured a lot of German hardware during its drive from the south of France in July 1944 into Germany in 1945. The Mauser Werke at Oberndorf was under French military control and produced or repaired various weapons for the French Army until the factory was dismantled in late 1946 after Soviet protests. After World War II the French Army in Indochina was a poor man's army, and many German weapons and ammunition stocks were used there, including the MP 40, P 08 and P 38 pistols, and StG 44 and Gew 43 rifles. In the 1945–48 period there was a mix of British, German and US weapons in service with the Corps Expéditionnaire Français en Extrême-Orient (CEFEO; French Far East Expeditionary Corps). Many of the post-war French-assembled MP 40s sported aluminium foregrips and pistol grips instead of Bakelite

Captured North Vietnamese Army (NVA) weapons, 1960. From top to bottom: Chinese PPS-43, German MP 40, Vietnamese K-50M. Of interest is what appears to be a replacement barrel for the MP 40 that was possibly fashioned by the North Vietnamese. (US Army Heritage and Education Center)

models. The MP 40 was not in use in the French Army at the time of the Algerian conflict (1956–62), although the Warsaw Pact countries supplied them to the Front de Libération Nationale (FLN; National Liberation Front) – Algerian rebels armed and trained in Tunisia – together with Kar 98k rifles, StG 44 assault rifles and MG 42 general-purpose machine guns.

One documented account of the French MP 40's persistent presence in Indochina/Vietnam comes from a veteran of the Vietnam War. Captain Edwin W. Besch commanded the Headquarters Company, 4th Marines, 3rd Marine Division in July 1966 during Operation *Hastings*, conducted in the northern part of South Vietnam. He purchased an MP 40, plus three magazines and 250 rounds, from a Marine Intelligence staff sergeant for US$65. The NCO didn't reveal his source, but the weapon was most probably retrieved through Army of the Republic of Vietnam (ARVN) sources, having been left behind by French colonial troops. Captain Besch carried it to augment the German Walther P 38 pistol he bought in the States 'and smuggled the pistol into Vietnam because it carried 3 more rounds than the Marine Corps issue M1911A1 .45 cal. pistol'.

On 23 July 1966, Captain Besch carried his MP 40 while 'riding along' on a psychological warfare mission in a Marine UH-34 helicopter that strayed behind the North Vietnamese 324B Division area and just below the Demilitarized Zone (DMZ). While sitting on an ammunition can and looking out the helicopter's large open door, he could see into North

Captain Ed Besch, USMC, armed with an MP 40 he used while in Vietnam, 1966. Hundreds of these captured German SMGs were brought over for use by the French Foreign Legion in Indochina after World War II and a few of these weapons stayed behind to see further service in the wars in South-East Asia. (AdeQ Historical Archives)

Vietnam and watched Navy F8 Crusader jets conducting nearby bombing runs. Suddenly, there was a scraping noise on the belly of the helicopter; he saw its tail rotor fly off, and an Air Force O-1 'Bird Dog' spotter plane, which had been directing the Navy air strike, lose a wing and explode in a ball of fire. Besch's helicopter had collided with the spotter plane.

Without its tail rotor, Besch's helicopter went into an uncontrolled spin, crashing into a mountainside about 1,500ft below. All of the Marines were lifted off the steep mountainside by hoists from two UH-1 'Huey' helicopters. Captain Besch suffered a 'probable cracked rib and possible spinal injury' and was medevac'd to a hospital ship. The regiment's Air Officer declared 'It was a miracle you all survived.'

Captain Besch was severely wounded on 23 August 1966 while commanding Echo Company, 4th Marines, during close combat, and sent to Great Lakes Naval Hospital, Illinois. The partially disassembled MP 40 and P 38 were thoughtfully sent to Captain Besch in a box marked 'Clothing'. He managed to get the MP 40 registered with the Bureau of Alcohol, Tobacco, and Firearms (ATF), paying for a $200 Federal Tax Stamp. At the time of writing this interesting weapon that served under four flags (Germany, France, South Vietnam and the United States), along with other mementoes of the Vietnam War, is still in the possession of Mr Besch.

The Norwegian Army used the MP 40 from 1945 until about 1970, and other parts of the Norwegian armed forces, such as the Norwegian

The Norwegian Army continued using captured MP 40s well into the late 1980s. The extreme cold encountered meant that the weapons would have to be kept clean and free from debris such as ice during use. In addition, the SMGs would have to have minimal lubrication, avoiding the use of anything likely to become gel-like in sub-freezing or even sub-zero weather and prevent the mechanism from operating. (AdeQ Historical Archives)

Home Guard, still issued the MP 40 as late as the early 1990s. Of interest is the cone-shaped blank-firing adapter manufactured to be used with the MP 40 while the weapon was in service with the Norwegians.

In conflicts around the world, the MP 38 and MP 40 continues to make an appearance. Some MP 40s were in use by the Kosovo Liberation Army in the Kosovo War of 1999. During the 'Arab Spring' uprisings and the revolt against General Gaddafi's government that took some of the Arab countries by surprise in 2011, a well-worn and magazine-less MP 38 was paraded in front of journalists' cameras by an anti-Gaddafi rebel fighter.

THE MP 40 IN NON-MILITARY USAGE

US law-enforcement agencies

A few civilian law-enforcement agencies, such as the Los Angeles Police Department (LAPD) in the United States, acquired MP 40s through confiscation, donation or local purchase. These weapons were never considered to be part of the main-use inventory, but rather as a back-up or 'last choice', since the main SMGs in use by the majority of law-enforcement agencies between the 1950s and the 1970s were the Thompson (Model 1928 and/or M1A1), M2 Carbine, Reising and the M3 'Grease Gun'. These ex-military SMGs were considered surplus after World War II and the Korean War; they were a cheap alternative compared to purchasing a newly manufactured SMG, as well as being readily available in whole and in parts.

In the early 1970s, two MP 40s were used by the LAPD SWAT team for a short time. Between 1973 and 1975 the Symbionese Liberation Army (SLA), a group that considered itself a revolutionary vanguard army, was

A US infantryman takes back an armful of MP 40s to the rear. After World War II a substantial number of these weapons found new homes in the United States. (NARA)

Non-guns: dummies and replicas

Beginning in the mid-1960s, toy companies began replicating full-scale non-firing models of the MP 40 for the collector market. Many of these were very accurate functioning copies; they were, however, rigged so they could not chamber or fire live rounds. In addition, soft-metal alloys were used during manufacture to ensure these models were unusable as firearms. Eventually, these were modified to fire caps or soft pellets.

The Japanese are the largest manufacturers of non-firing display models as well as air-soft versions. Some of these makers are well known to collectors and World War II re-enactors – names such as Shoei, Nakata, MGC and Marushin. The oldest and best-known model-gun manufacturer was the Model Gun Corporation (MGC). Founded in 1959 as 'Japan Modelgun Collection Association', it changed its name to MGC in the early 1980s. Initially, MGC sold imported toy guns (Mattel, Hubley, Nichols) and worked on making them more realistic. MGC was one of the first Japanese companies (besides Hudson) to produce self-designed model guns, in 1962. In the 1960s they released a few unique steel-made models (MP 40, Sten Mk III, Sterling). Their first employee and the designer of most of these models was Tazuo (Tanio) Kobayashi. The company went bankrupt in 1994; it was briefly revived until closing permanently in 2007, with interests lingering on until 2010.

The earliest of these model MP 40s was made by MGC. These authentic models were made with a plugged barrel and fired plug cap cartridges. The receiver, stock and barrel assembly were all metal parts, with the handguard and grips being plastic. Each model came with one 32-round magazine, 100 caps and 20 plug fire cartridges that were reusable. These 'MGC 68'-marked MP 40s were able to be taken down and disassembled like the original.

Another model gun company is Marushin of Tokyo, which still makes MP 40 models. The Marushin MP 40 version is constructed of ABS (acrylonitrile butadiene styrene is a common thermoplastic) and zinc alloys. The bolt safety works, the barrel nut looks correct, the muzzle nut screws on and the pistol grip has two actual screws holding it on the lower assembly. It also has a solid feel to it, due to the pistol grip being made out of zinc and through the use of stamped-steel parts. There are four versions of the Marushin MP 40: the pre-assembled 'plug cap firing' (the most common version); the kit version; the early all-zinc (PFC) version; and the non-blowback air-soft version.

A Spanish company, Denix SA, founded in 1966, also manufactured MP 40 model guns. After some years of consolidation, in 1978, coinciding with the establishment of the joint stock of the company, the company moved production to a new factory built in the industrial area of Ciutadella de Menorca. The company's catalogue, including all its variants, contains more than 300 models of weapons and accessories; among the offerings are authentic non-firing full-scale copies of the MP 40 and MP 41.

active in the United States. The SLA committed bank robberies, two murders and other acts of violence. The group also kidnapped the media heiress Patty Hearst. On 17 May 1974, officers of the LAPD surrounded a house where most SLA members were holed up. A massive shootout ensued, and the building went up in flames – shown live on television. The news film also captured footage of a member of the LAPD SWAT using one of the two MP 40s in the incident. A report on the activities of the SLA and the events leading up to the shootout stated that in excess of 9,000 rounds were fired; it noted that the SWAT team stationed at the rear of the residence carried two MP 40s, through which they fired a total of 440 rounds.

Private collectors

On account of the legends surrounding the MP 40 after World War II, there simply weren't enough existing wartime German SMGs to fulfil demand among American collectors. Contrary to popular belief, these weapons are legal to own as long as they are properly registered with the ATF and that the owners undergo an extensive background check by the Federal Bureau of Investigation (FBI).

In the late 1970s, an American company made full-automatic MP 40s. The Wilson Arms Company in Brunswick, Georgia, was a private company that was established in 1978. It manufactured the receiver tubes and built fully functioning and legally transferable full-automatic MP 40s from original parts kits until 1986. There were a fair number of MP 40 tube 'manufacturers' between 1968 and 1986. Another company was the Automatic Weapons Company (AWC) that was a Class 2 manufacturer in Albuquerque, New Mexico in the 1970s and 1980s. AWC manufactured re-welded original as well as new receiver tubes for the MP 40. A few of these receiver tubes manufactured by Wilson Arms and AWC were used in creating MP 41s as well.

In 1986, in the United States, the Firearm Owners' Protection Act amended the National Firearms Act (NFA) and the Gun Control Act (GCA) of 1968 to prohibit the transfer or possession of machine guns manufactured after 1986. Exceptions were made for transfers of machine guns to, or possession of machine guns by, government agencies, and those lawfully

The distinctive appearance and formidable reputation of the MP 38 and MP 40 would fuel post-war interest in these weapons. Here, a Luftwaffe enlisted man is carrying his MP 40 with its folding stock extended out. Of interest is the change of bolt-charging handle, which was actually a two-piece safety retracting handle. Note the pair of canvas magazine pouches, one of which would have a compartment for a magazine loader. (AdeQ Historical Archives)

possessed before the effective date of the prohibition – 19 May 1986. Wilson Arms Company, as well as other American firearms companies such as AWC, manufactured hundreds of legally transferable registered MP 40 receiver tubes prior to the cut-off date; these are found in many collections to this day.

Between 2005 and 2010, an American firm made a limited number of live-firing semi-automatic MP 40s. Schoessler's Supply Room (SSR) of Springboro, Ohio, made a version with a 40.6cm barrel and folding stock, which utilized parts from an original MP 40 parts kit. The new receiver tube, internals and original bolt assembly were modified to fire in semi-automatic mode only. It came with a display dummy barrel as well as with a welded blank-adapted short barrel for use in re-enactments for blank firing only. In addition, SSR also manufactured a folding-stock version with original-length barrel and a pistol configuration with a fixed stock and original barrel length – probably the most authentic firing version, since it was comprised of original parts. The folding-stock version with original-length barrel is considered to be a short-barrelled rifle (SBR) by the ATF and requires federal paperwork and a tax stamp. The company also produced a blank-firing version using an ingenious system that will be discussed in the next section. SSR closed its doors in January 2010.

In about 2005 a German firm, Sport-Systeme Dittrich, began manufacturing a semi-automatic version of the MP 38 known as the BD38. It is an authentic copy of the wartime MP 38 and functions the same as the original. The weapon is currently manufactured and distributed by HZA Kulmbach GmbH (founded in 2010). Limited numbers of the MP 38 as well as the MP 44 were imported into Canada and the United States. For US import this weapon was sold as a 'pistol' because of its short barrel and the folding stock being permanently fixed in its folded position.

The latest version of the MP 40 to be remanufactured is a .22 Long Rifle (LR) version made by German Sport Guns (GSG) and intended for sport shooting and plinking (shooting casually at random targets). Its products are copies or replicas of famous military firearms, but are often subject to much less legal scrutiny because of the cartridge they use. Additionally, .22 LR is often less than one-tenth the price of centrefire ammunition, making it a cost-effective way to teach shooting skills and have fun at a low outlay to the user. The company also produces airsoft replicas. In January 2013, the .22 LR versions of the MP 40 were debuted by GSG and ATI (GSG's US distributor) at the SHOT Show in Las Vegas, Nevada. Two prototype versions were shown at the firearms exposition: the first had a 40.6cm barrel, a fake suppressor resembling the World War II-style L 42 and a folding stock (rifle version), while the second had an original-length barrel of 25.1cm and had the stock permanently fixed in its folded position (pistol version). The GSG MP 40s, marked with the 'SCHMEISSER' name, are expected to be released into the US market in 2014.

THE MP 40 IN POPULAR CULTURE

The MP 40 has been portrayed by popular culture as the most common weapon in the hands of German soldiers of World War II, but in reality that accolade was taken by the Mauser Kar 98k, a bolt-action rifle, which was issued and used much more widely. Large stockpiles of MP 40s captured by the Soviets were made available for wartime and post-war film productions. The first documented appearance of the MP 40 in film was in the 1943 Soviet film *Dva boytsa* ('Two Soldiers'). The film depicted most of the German soldiers armed with MP 40s. In the 1944 film *Ivan Nikulin: Russkiy Matros* ('Ivan Nikulin: Russian Sailor') – set in the summer of 1942 and recounting the story of a small force of Black Sea Fleet sailors surrounded by German troops before breaking out of the encirclement – the MP 40 was used in large numbers by both the Germans and Soviets throughout the movie.

In the 1958 Czech film *Černý prapor* ('The Black Battalion') Czech members of the French Foreign Legion were depicted armed with MP 40s while fighting in the French Indochina War. Thereafter the MP 38 and MP 40 continued appearing in war films, right through to the present. Most of these films tend to depict the MP 40 as common as the bolt-action rifle, such as *Where Eagles Dare* (1968), where nearly everyone is armed with the SMG. Other films, such as *The Longest Day* (1962) and *Saving Private Ryan* (1998), showed a more realistic balance of weaponry.

Silver-screen portrayals of the MP 38 and MP 40 were not confined to war-related films; these weapons have also been associated with film portrayals of post-war criminals, spies and other villains. In the film *Dirty*

One of the most poignant of all the Warsaw Uprising monuments was unveiled by the walls of the Barbakan in 1981. It depicted a bronze figure of a boy soldier clutching an MP 40 and weighed down by an adult-sized captured German helmet. The memorial commemorated the Polish children who served as messengers and as front-line troops. (AdeQ Historical Archives)

Harry (1971), the Scorpio Killer uses an MP 40 to shoot at San Francisco Police Inspectors Harry Callahan and Chico Gonzalez during the shootout on the rooftops, and later he fires it at Gonzalez during the fight at the base of the Mt Davidson Cross. In one scene, Scorpio reloads his MP 40, but racks the action back and forth. People familiar with the weapon know it fires from an open bolt, so he either failed to pull the action back all the way, or held the trigger down as he pulled the action back.

The MP 40 has even appeared in the genres of adventure, science-fiction and horror films. Numerous MP 40s were depicted inaccurately in pre-war Egypt in the film *Raiders of the Lost Ark* (1981). The MP 40's inclusion is anachronistic, since the film is set in 1936 and neither the MP 40 nor its more expensive predecessor, the MP 38, existed at the time. The MP 40 appeared again in *Indiana Jones and the Last Crusade* (1989). In the 2012 film *Iron Sky*, depicting a 2018 Nazi invasion of Earth from the dark side of the Moon, the invaders are armed with MP 40s. Occasionally, the MP 41 has featured in films as well, including *Enemy at the Gates* (2001), *Hart's War* (2002), and even *Mr Bean's Holiday* (2007)!

Television series depicting World War II such as *Combat!*, *Hogan's Heroes* and *The Rat Patrol* featured the MP 40, as did the American television mini-series *Holocaust* (1978). In addition, the MP 40 appeared in spy shows such as *The Man from U.N.C.L.E.* and *Mission Impossible*. The MP 40 even showed up in science-fiction series such as *Star Trek*, *Caprica* and *Doctor Who*. Amazingly, the MP 40 appeared in animated television programmes and even Japanese Animé, from *Appleseed* (1988) to *Archer* (2007).

In art, the MP 40 has become closely associated with the Nazi regime. In the Soviet Union during the Cold War, thousands of paintings were commissioned to evoke the Great Patriotic War against Hitler, with many depicting heroic Soviet soldiers defeating the Nazi soldiers normally armed with an MP 40. Others showed German troops executing defiant Soviet civilians with their MP 40s. The MP 40 also features prominently in two Polish war memorials relating to the Warsaw Uprising. The Warsaw Uprising Monument on Krasinski Square consists of two groups of sculptures: one group of sculptures depicts an attack by an insurgent unit, of whom one is armed with a MP 40-style weapon, while the other shows an 'Exodus', whereby the insurgents are seen making a withdrawal into the sewers underneath the streets. The Little Insurgent Monument (Mały Powstaniec) commemorates the child soldiers who fought and died in the Warsaw Uprising; it is of a young boy wearing a helmet too large for his head and holding an MP 40. It is reputed to be of a fighter who went by the pseudonym of Antek, who was killed on 8 August 1944 at the age of 13.

The MP 40 also features on at least one memorial honouring those who fought for the Germans, rather than against them. In Estonia, a monument depicts a soldier prominently holding an MP 40 across his chest. It was dedicated to those who served in the Finnish Army, the Wehrmacht, and particularly the Waffen-SS. It was originally unveiled in Pärnu on 2002, but taken down only nine days later; it is currently on the grounds of the privately owned Museum of the Fight for Estonia's Freedom, located near Tallinn.

LIMITATIONS

Having acknowledged the importance of the MP 40, in every sphere from wartime use to cinema, we also have to accept what ultimately limited its influence – the rise of the assault rifle. Although SMGs continue in use to this day, primarily in the hands of special forces and criminals (both, ironically, tend to have the same focus on close-range combat), the assault rifle effectively undermined the rationale for the SMG. We see this shift in the rise of the StG 44 between 1943 and 1945. The StG 44 offered full-auto fire, just like the MP 40, but with better range (up to and exceeding 600m), superior penetration and improved terminal effect. In essence, the assault rifle offered the best of the rifle and SMG in one unit.

The end of World War II prevented this reality becoming immediately transparent, but in the late 1940s the emergence of the AK-47 – which would become history's most widely distributed weapon – left the world in no doubt as to the future. During several post-war conflicts, SMG armed soldiers found themselves at a critical disadvantage when faced with AK-wielding opponents. The writing was on the wall for the standard-issue SMG, and steadily almost every nation adopted an assault rifle (or at least an automatic rifle) as its standard-issue weapon. It is this factor that consigned the MP 40 to history. Yet it remains one of history's most recognizable small arms, a testimony to its design qualities as well as its aesthetics.

CONCLUSION

Throughout World War II, the MP 38 and later the MP 40 played a vital role in nearly every campaign that involved the Wehrmacht. From the deadly winter of the Eastern Front to the desert sands of North Africa, the

These relic SMGs found in battlefields from Kurland to Normandy show three basic types of magazine wells that can facilitate speedy identification from afar. From bottom to top: MP 38 with the distinctive hole, an early MP 40 with slab-sided magazine, standard MP 40 with ribbed sides. (AdeQ Historical Archives)

MP 40 made its impact in combat. As well as portability and reliability, the weapon offered relatively low recoil even fired on full-automatic, owing to the slower rate of fire and its 9mm round. For an SMG, it provided respectable accuracy compared to similar Allied weapons such as the American Thompson, which fired the .45-calibre ACP round. Because of its light weight, the MP 40 was held in high esteem and was particularly favoured by airborne and motorized troops. After World War II, many MP 40s captured by the Allies were redistributed to the paramilitary and irregular forces of several countries; these guns were eventually used in conflicts as far afield as Greece, Israel, Korea and Vietnam, and the MP 40 continued in service with elements of the Norwegian military into the 1990s.

The MP 40 was a highly influential weapon in design terms, too. From the outset the weapon was designed for mass production, which would be taken to an even higher level with the use of simpler and less-expensive stamped parts and the additional streamlining of production techniques. The ultimate goal was the mass arming of the Wehrmacht with a capable, inexpensive, yet reliable SMG, and just over 1 million were made of all versions during the course of the war. For the most part, the weapon met this goal, except for one important problem: when jarred, the gun could start firing by itself. The next generation of SMG designs would fix this dangerous issue. Many countries involved in World War II developed SMGs with similar features to those of the MP 40 – such as a folding stock and the use of the magazine well as a front handgrip – and, crucially, relying upon the production techniques used for the German weapon. The most famous examples are the Soviet PPS-43 and the American M3.

Since 1945, the MP 40 has become an iconic part of popular culture, from art and cinema to television and video games. Its reputation, won in wartime and perpetuated ever since in countless representations in popular culture, looks set to last well into the 21st century.

Soldiers of Infanterie-Regiment 638, a unit made up of French volunteers, are pictured on the Eastern Front. The MP 40 pictured here is a transitional model with its distinctive slabside magazine well. (AdeQ Historical Archives)

The MP 38 and MP 40 have become emblematic of the German war effort in World War II. As is evident here, the magazine extending from underneath made the MP 40 awkward to fire from concealed or fortified positions; the shooter has had to clear out an area to position his magazine within his foxhole. (AdeQ Historical Archives)

BIBLIOGRAPHY

Printed sources

Anonymous (1940). 'D (Luft) 5602: Die Ausbildung mit der Maschinenpistole 38 und 40 (M.P. 38 und 40)'. Berlin: Dr M. Matthiesen & Co.

Anonymous (1948). *Nuevo Sub-fusil 'STAR' mod. Z 45 (5th Edition)*. Eibar: Star Bonifacio Echeverría Sociedad Anónima.

Anonymous (1970). *Drzavni Seketarijat za Narodnu Odbranu. Automati 7,62 mm M.56 i M.49/57*. Belgrade: Vojna stamparija.

Baum, John, trans. (2006). D 167/1: *Machine Pistol 40: Description, Operation, and Handling Instructions, From Sept. 25, 1942 & D 167/2: Machine Pistol 40 and Machine Pistol 38: Individual Parts, From Dec. 11, 1942*. Lisbon, OH: Author.

Besch, Edwin W. (2012). Correspondence with A.M. de Quesada regarding use of MP 40 in Vietnam, 16 March 2012.

Bruce, Robert (1996). *German Automatic Weapons of World War Two*. London: Windrow & Greene.

Bull, Stephen (2004). *World War II Infantry Tactics: Squad and Platoon*. Oxford: Osprey Publishing.

Bull, Stephen (2011). *World War II: The Last War Heroes*. Oxford: Osprey Publishing.

Cormack, A.J.R. (1972). *Small Arms Profile 8: ERMA Submachine Guns*. Windsor: Profile Publications.

Denckler, Heinz (1941). *Die Maschinenpistole 40: Beschreibung und Handhabung*. Berlin: Heinz Denckler-Verlag.

Ellis, Chris with Chamberlain, Peter (1999). *Schmeisser Submachine Gun*. London: PRC Publishing.

Fischer, Karl (1944). *Waffen- und Schiesstechnischer Leitfaden für die Ordnungspolizei*. Berlin: Verlag R. Eisenschmidt.

Götz, Hans Dieter (1990). *German Military Rifles and Machine Pistols, 1871–1945*. West Chester, PA: Schiffer Publishing.

Iannamico, Frank (1998). *Blitzkrieg: The MP 40 Maschinenpistole of World War II*. Harmony, ME: Moose Lake Publishing.

Iannamico, Frank (1999). *MP 38–MP 40 Machine Pistol Operators Manual: An English Translation of the Rare German Luftwaffe Manual*. Harmony, ME: Moose Lake Publishing.

Ingram, Mike (2001). *The MP 40 Submachine Gun*. Osceola, WI: MBI Publishing Company.

Johnson, George B. & Lockhoven, Hans Bert (1965). *International Armament: With history, data, technical information and photographs of 400 weapons, Vol. II*. Cologne: International Small Arms Publishers.

Markham, George (1989). *Guns of the Reich: Firearms of the German Forces, 1939–1945*. London: Arms & Armour Press.

Pegler, Martin (2010). *The Thompson Submachine Gun: From Prohibition Chicago to World War II*. Oxford: Osprey Publishing.

Reibert, W. (1940). *Der Dienstunterricht um Heere: Ausgabe für den Schützen der Schützenkompanie*. Berlin: Verlag von E. S. Mittler & Sohn.

Smith, W.H.B. & Smith, Joseph E. (1969). *Small Arms of the World* (Revised Edition). Harrisburg, PA: Stackpole.

US Army (1943). 'First Report on Test of (Schmeisser) German M.P. 40 Sub-Machine Gun, 30 December 1942–14 January 1943'. Ordnance Research Center, Aberdeen Proving Ground, Project No. P.R. 14, O.P. 5826.

Vries, G. de & Martens, B.J. (2001). *The MP 38, 40, 40/1 and 41 Submachine Gun*. Arnhem: Special Interest Publicaties BV.

Weaver, W. Darrin (2008). *Kunststoffe: A Collector's Guide to German World War II Plastics and Their Markings*. Atglen, PA: Schiffer Publishing.

Zaitsev, Vassili (2009). *Notes of a Russian Sniper*. London: Frontline Books.

Online references

The following websites are highly recommended for more information regarding the MP 38, MP 40 and MP 41:

'Die Maschinenpistole 40: The MP 38, 40 and 41 Submachine Gun' http://www.MP 40.nl/ (accessed 27 March 2013).

'Internet Movie Firearms Database: MP 40' http://www.imfdb.org/wiki/ MP 40 (accessed 27 March 2013).

'World Guns' worldguns.ru (accessed 17 March 2014).

The MP 41 was the next variation of the MP 38/MP 40 family. Though never officially adopted by the Wehrmacht, it was used by police and paramilitary formations as well as foreign allies such as Romania. These members of the SD (SS Security Service) are seen armed with MP 41s and MP 34s during the Warsaw Uprising. (AdeQ Historical Archives)

INDEX

Figures in **bold** refer to illustrations.